The Universe and Its Origin

The Universe and its Origin

Edited by

H. MESSEL

*Professor of Physics and
Head of the School of Physics
University of Sydney*

and

S. T. BUTLER

*Professor of Theoretical Physics
University of Sydney*

LONDON
MACMILLAN & CO LTD
NEW YORK ST MARTIN'S PRESS
1964

MACMILLAN & COMPANY LIMITED

St Martin's Street London WC2
also Bombay Calcutta Madras Melbourne

THE MACMILLAN COMPANY OF CANADA LIMITED
Toronto

ST MARTIN'S PRESS INC
New York

PRINTED IN GREAT BRITAIN
BY W. & J. MACKAY & CO LTD, CHATHAM

Contributors

G. GAMOW, Department of Physics, University of Colorado, Boulder, U.S.A.

B. J. BOK, Department of Astronomy, The Australian National University, Canberra.

T. GOLD, Centre for Radiophysics and Space Research, Cornell University, New York, U.S.A.

C. B. A. MCCUSKER, The Falkiner Nuclear Department, School of Physics, University of Sydney, Australia.

Acknowledgements

THE line drawings in this book are reproduced by kind permission of The Shakespeare Head Press, Sydney, Australia.

Preface

FOR many years now, the Nuclear Research Foundation of the University of Sydney has been concerned with the growing shortage of scientists and especially science teachers in Australia. The reasons for the shortage are many and complex. But the Foundation felt that a major step forward could be taken by the institution of refresher courses for the Science Teachers. It was hoped that the provision of first class courses by some of the world's outstanding scientists would not only bring the Science Teacher up to date, but would also inspire him and he would in turn inspire his students.

The Foundation has been amply rewarded for its endeavour in Australia, and the Summer Science Schools have stimulated great interest throughout the nation. In fact they have become 'Science for the millions', the lectures being televised and shown many times throughout Australia.

Although specifically written to cater for secondary school teachers, the lectures – some of which are presented in this book – are of considerable interest to a much wider category of readers. They provide a basic introduction to the fields discussed and to recent advances. Thus, they are of value not only to the interested layman but also, for fields other than his own, to the specialized scientist.

It should be pointed out that the subjects covered in the Summer Schools do not necessarily integrate with one another. They were never meant to do so. We hope that these lectures may stimulate the same interest overseas as they have in Australia. If so, our efforts will be amply rewarded.

H. MESSEL and S. T. BUTLER

Contents

Contents

CHAPTER 1

Distance Scale of the Universe

Stellar Parallaxes

Whereas information on the size of the Earth and on distances from it to the Moon, the Sun, and the planets was available to a large extent to ancient and medieval astronomers, the distances of even the nearest stars were not determined until the beginning of the last century. In 1838 a German astronomer, F. W. Bessel, succeeded in measuring the parallax of a star known as 61 Cygni. Comparing the position of that star in respect to other background stars, he noticed a small annual displacement caused by the motion of the Earth on its orbit around the Sun. The positions of the star observed six months apart differed by 0·6 angular second, from which Bessel calculated that the distance to it is 690,000 radii of the Earth's orbit, a distance which is covered by light in the course of eleven years. The improvement of astronomic instruments since Bessel's time now permits us to measure the distances to a great many stars, but the precision is not sufficient to go far beyond the Milky Way, the part of the stellar system to which our Sun belongs, the 'local swimming hole' as astronomer W. Baade calls it.

Cepheid Distance Scale

The possibility of measuring considerably larger stellar distances was presented by the study of peculiar types of variable stars known as Cepheids named after δ Cepheus, the first observed star of that type. In contrast to ordinary 'eclipsing variables', the brightness of which changes because they periodically eclipse one another, the variability of cepheids is due to periodic pulsations of their giant bodies. Early in this century, Miss Henrietta S. Leavitt of Harvard College Observatory made an important discovery by noticing that the period of cepheid variables depends in a unique way on their absolute luminosity. Observing the cepheids belonging to the Magellanic Clouds – a couple of small irregular galaxies of stars located nearest to us in space – and plotting their visual luminosities against their periods, she obtained a smooth curve indicating that pulsation period increases rapidly with the visual brightness of the star. Since cepheids in the Magellanic Clouds are at about the same distance from us, their visual brightnesses are proportional to their absolute brightnesses, so that the statement remains true for them also. This discovery gave to astronomy a magic yardstick for measuring large distances. Indeed, if we see a group of stars containing a cepheid, and measure the pulsation period of that star, we can read from the period-luminosity curve its absolute brightness and, by comparing it with visual brightness, find the distance simply by using inverse square law. But, in order to construct period-luminosity curves in terms of absolute bright-nesses, one should know the absolute brightness of at least one cepheid. Unfortunately, cepheids are very rare in the sky, and the nearest of them, the well-known Polar Star (period about four days), is too far away to show any parallactic displacement. Thus, the astronomers had to use some roundabout methods for estimating the distances of a few cepheids and thereby calibrating the period-luminosity curve. The method used by E. Hertzsprung at Leyden Observatory was based on the comparison of radial and tangential velocities of distant stars. Radial velocities of stars can be directly measured by the Doppler shift in their spectra, and the results are independent of their distance from us. Tangential veloci-ties manifest themselves in small secular displacement of nearer stars in respect to the background of much more distant stars (proper motion), and the farther away the star the smaller is its annual displacement. Using the statistical method, and assuming that the velocities of stars are more or less randomly distributed in all directions, one can get an idea of the distance of a group of stars by comparing their average radial velocities and their average tangential displacements. Applying this method to a galac-tic group of stars containing a cepheid variable, Hertzsprung came to the conclusion that 'the average absolute magnitude of a cepheid with 6·6 days' period, is × 2·3 (i.e. this cepheid is about a thousand times brighter than the Sun)'. This conclusion led to the calibration of the period-luminosity curve, and its use for the measurement of very large astro-nomical distances.

Distances to Centre of the Milky Way and to the Great Andromeda Nebula

The first use of the method was made in 1918 by H. Shapley of Harvard College Observatory, for estimating the distances to the globular clusters, spherically symmetrical groups of stars floating in space around the centre of our Milky Way system. Using the cepheids belonging to globular clusters, Shapley found that these clusters fill up a sphere with the centre located 52,000 light years from us in the direction of the con-stellation of Sagittarius. This finding proved that our solar system is located not near the centre of the Milky Way as was believed before (the recurrence of the Ptolemeic system of the world), but rather far on the outskirts. A few years later E. Hubble of Mount Wilson Observatory applied the same method to measuring the distance of the Great Nebula in Andromeda, a galaxy of stars similar to our Milky Way, floating far away in space. Observing cepheids found in the arms of the Andromeda nebula, and estimating their absolute brightness from the observed pulsation periods, Hubble found that this great stellar galaxy is about one million light years away from us. The same method was used for measuring the distances of other galaxies scattered farther out in space which were, however, not so distant that individual cepheids could not be observed.

The use of Miss Leavitt's curve calibrated by Hertzsprung's point ($-2\cdot3$ magnitude for $6\cdot6$ days cepheid) opened new vistas in observational astronomy, but soon the difficulties began to accumulate. First of all, difficulty arose with the theory of cepheid pulsations developed by Sir Arthur Eddington. Although we still do not know what maintains the pulsations of these stars, one can predict theoretically the relation between their pulsation periods and their mean densities. Indeed, the relation between the pulsation period and the mean density of a giant gas sphere held together by the forces of gravity is not much different from the relation between the period and the length of a pendulum swinging in the gravitational field, and should hold, no matter whether we do or do not know what drives the pendulum or what maintains the pulsation of the star. However, Eddington's calculations based on the mass-luminosity relation led to values of density inconsistent with estimates made by other methods.

Another difficulty arose in comparing the sizes of the Andromeda Nebula and other nearby galaxies, calculated on the basis of their estimated distances, based on the period-luminosity of the cepheids' relation to the size of our own galaxy. It appeared that our stellar system, the Milky Way, is much larger than any of its neighbours. Of course, it could be, but why should our galaxy be so much bigger than any other?

Probably the worst contradiction arose in the problem of the age of the world of galaxies. As will be discussed in more detail in the next chapter, galaxies recede from each other with rather high speeds proportional to their mutual distances. Dividing the average distances between the galaxies by their average recession velocities, one came to the conclusion that matter, which is now highly dispersed through the space of the Universe, was tightly packed together about $1\cdot8$ thousand million years ago. This date in the past must, one thought, correspond to the original chaotic state of the Universe, the beginning of all things. On the other hand, we find on the shelves of mineralogical museums rocks whose age, estimated by radioactive methods, is three and more thousand million years. How can our Universe contain rocks which are considerably older than the Universe itself?

Baade's Correction

These contradictions, which plagued cosmology for almost three

Fig. 1.1a. A typical stellar Population I representing a mixture of stars and inter-stellar clouds. (Luminosity in Monoceros) 200-inch photograph

decades, were brilliantly resolved by W. Baade of Mount Wilson Observatory only a few years ago. In his studies of stars forming our Milky Way as well as of other galaxies, Baade found that there are two entirely different types of stellar population. Spiral arms, to which our Sun belongs, are characterized by a large amount of interstellar material, highly rarified gas and dust, which equals in amount the matter concentrated

Fig. 1.1b. Spiral arms of a Galaxy (in Ursa Major) are formed by typical Population I. 200-inch photograph

into individual stars. Under the action of the forces of gravity, this
interstellar material must give rise to condensations which develop into
new stars, and, indeed, in these regions one does observe stars which are
so bright that they could not possibly have existed for more than a few
million years. A typical example of this stellar population, known as
Population I, is shown in Figs. 1.1a and 1.1b, which show the stars and

Fig. 1.2a. A typical stellar Population II consisting of stars only. (Globular cluster in
Hercules) 200-inch photograph

the interstellar clouds in the constellation of Monoceros, and in a spiral galaxy.

On the other hand, globular clusters and elliptical galaxies (Figs. 1.2a, 1.2b) present an entirely different picture, being deprived of any interstellar material and formed entirely by stars which are presumably all of the same age, formed about five thousand million years ago. This is

Fig. 1.2b. Elliptical (armless) galaxy (in Cassiopeia) formed by a typical Population II. 200-inch photograph

known as Population II. The problem of the genetical difference between the two stellar populations represents the outstanding riddle of Cosmogony, and its solution will open our eyes to the important question of how the galaxies of stars were born. What we know now from direct observations is that stars belonging to these two different population types have rather different properties. Blue giant stars (the young ones) which are so prominent in Population I are completely absent in Population II. Supernovae which flare up in Population I (known as Supernovae type II) are quite different from the supernovae (type I) observed in stellar Population II. This mix-up is not devised by astronomers to confuse the layman, but is the result of the historical course of discoveries.

Finally, as was shown by Baade, the cepheids in Population I are different from the cepheids in Population II, and their period-luminosity curve runs about two stellar magnitudes higher (a factor 6 in brightness) (Fig. 1.3). The old single period-luminosity curve established on the basis of Hertzsprung's work runs very close to the Population II curve, so that the estimate of the distance of globular clusters and the dimensions of our galaxy made by Shapley remain essentially unchanged. On the other hand, the old values for the distances of the Great Andromeda Nebula, and other galaxies in which the cepheids type I are observed,

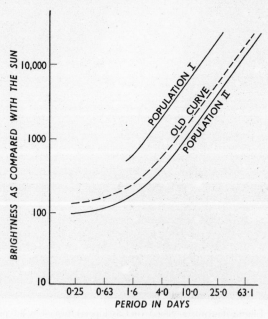

Fig. 1.3. Old (broken line) and new period luminosity curves

must be corrected by a factor of about 2·5. This discovery straightened out the old paradox concerning the abnormally large size of the Milky Way, and eliminated the contradiction between the astronomical and geological estimates of the age of the Universe. More recent studies made by A. R. Sandage suggest that the distances of galaxies must be further increased by a factor of 2·3.

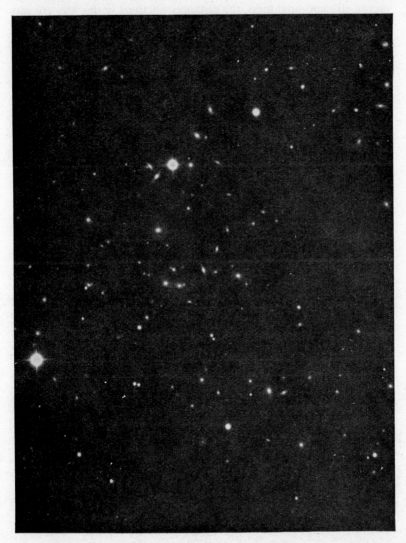

Fig. 1.4. Cluster of galaxies in Corona Borealis. 200-inch photograph

Clusters of Galaxies

The method of distance measurements described above remains valid, however, only as far out in space as the galaxies can be resolved into individual stars so that their cepheids can be observed. Beyond this limit, the only way of telling the distance of the galaxy is to see how faint it looks and to apply the inverse square law of luminosity. Since galaxies vary in size and brightness, the distances obtained in this way are very uncertain in the case of individual galaxies. Fortunately, however, they are often encountered in large groups or clusters, so that one can average the luminosities of the galaxies in the cluster, thus obtaining a more reliable distance estimate. Thus, for example, the large cluster of galaxies in the constellation of Virgo was found to be forty-nine million light-years away from us, whereas the cluster in the constellation of Coma is 290 million light years away. In Fig. 1.4 we see a cluster of galaxies in Corona Borealis located 800 thousand million light years away.

Curvature of Space

The possibility of measuring the distances of hundreds of millions of light years in the space around us leads to an exciting possibility of studying geometrical properties of the space of the Universe, and of finding out whether it is flat in the sense of the good old Euclidian geometry or

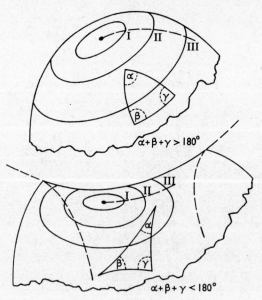

Fig. 1.5. Surfaces of positive (above) and negative (below) curvatures

curved in accordance with the non-Euclidian geometries of Riemann and Lobatchevsky. The idea of a curved three-dimensional space can best be understood by analogy with curved surfaces which have only two dimensions (Fig. 1.5). It is well known that the theorems of Euclidian plane geometry do not hold with regard to the surface of a sphere. Whereas in Euclidian geometry the sum of the angles of a triangle is always equal to 180°, the sum of the angles of a spherical triangle is always larger than that. This can easily be seen, for example, by considering a triangle on a globe formed by two meridianal arcs between the pole and the equator, and the part of the equator connecting them; each of the two angles at the base of that triangle is equal to 90°, to which is to be added the angle at the pole. Similarly, the area of a circle described on a spherical surface is not equal to the square of its radius times π as in plane geometry. Indeed, consider the parallels drawn on the globe for 80°, 70°, 60°, etc., of northern latitude. Their radii, measured from the pole along the surface of the globe, increase as the integers 1, 2, 3, etc., but their areas increase more slowly than 1, 4, 9, etc. The surfaces having these properties are said to have positive curvature.

Another type of curved surface is represented by the so-called saddle surface, which can be visualized as an ordinary saddle used for horseback-riding which is, however, extended beyond any limit up in front and behind the rider, and down on both sides. In contrast to a spherical surface which 'curves in' and finally closes on itself, a saddle surface 'curves out' and extends to infinity in all directions. It is easy to show that on such surfaces, which are said to have a negative curvature, the sum of the angles of a triangle is smaller than 180°, whereas the area of a circle increases faster than the square of its radius.

All the above statements can easily be visualized by us, since, as we are three-dimensional beings, we can look on the curved surfaces from the outside. For the imaginary two-dimensional beings, however, who live in the surface and have no idea that there is a third direction along the radius of the sphere, things would not be so apparent. They could, nevertheless, answer the question whether their surface is plane, or curves positively or negatively, by measuring the sum of angles of a triangle or studying how the area of a circle increases with its radius. Being three-dimensional creatures and asking ourselves about the curvature of the three-dimensional space in which we live, we must follow similar methods, studying the validity of Euclidian geometry as applied to the space of the Universe. The most convenient method consists in checking the Euclidian statement that the volume of a sphere increases as the cube of its radius. If this statement is found true for the

Universe at large, our three-dimensional space is 'flat'. If, however, the volume is found to increase more slowly or faster than the cube of the radius, the space should be ascribed a positive or negative curvature. The first case would suggest that the Universe is finite, having the volume of so many cubic light years, whereas in the second case the Universe should be considered as infinite.

Studies in this direction, first suggested by R. C. Tolman, were carried out by E. Hubble at the Mount Wilson Observatory many years ago. The method was to count the number of galaxies within the distances increasing as 1, 2, 3, etc., and to see if this number increases as the cubes of these numbers or not. The result of these 'galactic counts' was very astonishing. Hubble found that the number of galaxies increases notice-ably more slowly than the cube of their distance, indicating a positively curved Universe of such small overall dimensions that it stood in con-tradiction with all other astronomical data. It was, however, indicated at that time that Hubble's method of distance measurements contained a possible fallacy. Using the inverse square law of luminosity for the estimate of distance, he was making an implicit assumption that the galaxies do not change their luminosity with their age. Indeed, looking far out into space we look far back in time because of the finite velocity of light and, if the galaxies had a different luminosity at the time the light was emitted from them, the corresponding correction in distance should be made. It can be shown that an assumed decrease of galactic bright-nesses just by several per cent per thousand million years would swing Hubble's results from a positively curved finite space to a negatively curved infinite space. Unfortunately, much as we now know about the stellar content of galaxies and the evolution of stars, we cannot yet make any reasonable theoretical conclusion as to how the average brightness of a galaxy depends on its age, because of the evolutionary process. Thus, the question of finiteness or infiniteness of the Universe still remains open.

Mean Density of the Universe

We will conclude our present discussion by inquiring into the problem of the average density of matter in the Universe. The best way to get infor-mation about the galactic masses is to study a cluster of galaxies such as the Virgo and Coma clusters mentioned above. Galaxies forming these clusters show a rather regular spherical symmetrical distribution in space, getting denser and denser towards the centre of the sphere. They are apparently held together by the forces of gravity between them, which give us the key for finding out their total mass by using the 'virial' theorem. One can show on the basis of theoretical mechanics that, in the case of a system consisting of a number of moving material bodies held together by forces subject to the inverse square law, the average kinetic energy of motion is equal to one half of the absolute value of the average potential energy due to the mutual attraction.

If M is the combined mass of all the bodies forming the system, and v their average velocity, the total kinetic energy will be

$$K = \tfrac{1}{2} Mv^2 \tag{1.1}$$

On the other hand, one can show that the mutual potential energy of mass M distributed through a sphere of radius R is given by

$$U = - a \frac{GM^2}{R} \tag{1.2}$$

where G is Newton's constant of gravity and a a numerical coefficient of the order of one (for uniform distribution $a = \tfrac{5}{3}$ and has only slightly different values for various non-uniform distributions). According to the Virial Theorem

$$\tfrac{1}{2} Mv^2 = \frac{a}{2} \frac{GM^2}{R} \tag{1.3}$$

from which we find

$$M = \frac{Rv^2}{aG} \tag{1.4}$$

Thus we can find the mass of the system if we know its radius and the average velocity of its members. In the case of clusters of galaxies, we can measure the radial velocities of their members by observing the Doppler effect in their spectra. In the case of the Virgo cluster the average radial velocity in respect to the centre of gravity was found to be 550 km/sec. If the velocity distribution is isotropic in space, as it most likely is, the average tangential velocity must have the same value, so that the average velocity of internal space motion becomes 1000 km/sec. Since the radius of cluster is 3·2 million light years, one finds that its mass is 5×10^{14} solar masses, and that its mean density is 8×10^{-27} g/cm³. In the case of the Coma cluster one finds, by using a similar method, the mass of 6×10^{11} sun masses and the mean density of about 4×10^{-26} g/cm³. Thus the Coma cluster is lighter and more compact than that in Virgo. Using these values and comparing the distribution densities of galaxies in clusters with the average distribution density of galaxies throughout the space of the Universe, one can find the average density of matter in the Universe. The most recent figure obtained by the Dutch astronomer J. H. Oort is 3×10^{-31} g/cm³ or 0·2 hydrogen atoms per cubic metre.

CHAPTER 2

Time Scale of the Universe

The Age of the Earth

The second important problem concerning our Universe is its time scale, or the ages of its most important features. We may start from our neighbourhood and ask how old the Earth is. Geologists estimate the ages of rocks forming the crust of the Earth by measuring the amount of lead deposited as the result of radioactive decay of uranium and thorium contained in the igneous rocks of various origins. The older the rock, the larger the amount of deposited lead as compared with the amount of radioactive element still present. However, this method has a flaw, since in the series of elements leading from uranium to lead there is one member, radon, which is a gas, and could have partially escaped by diffusion through the rock, thus lowering the estimate of the age. A better method is based on radioactivity of rubidium which, emitting an electron, decays into stable strontium. The best present estimate of the age of the Earth's crust, obtained by this method, is $4 \cdot 5 \times 10^9$ years.

Another method, also pertaining to our globe, is based on the salinity of the ocean's water. Salt is continuously brought into oceans by the rivers, which contain a small amount of salt dissolved by rain waters coming down the mountain slopes. Water evaporates from the ocean's surface, leaving the salt behind, and goes through successive cycles of condensation and evaporation, while more and more salt is accumulated in the ocean. Dividing the total amount of salt in the ocean water by the annual input of salt by rivers, one finds that it must have taken several thousand million years to build up the present salinity. This method, first suggested by the astronomer E. Halley more than three centuries ago, and improved by using current geological and hydrological information, can give only the order of magnitude of the ocean's age because of great uncertainties in the rate of erosion during the past geological eras.

The Age of the Moon

Still another method is based on the history of the Earth-Moon system, according to the theory proposed half a century ago by George

Darwin, the son of Charles. Everybody knows that tides in the oceans are mostly due to the gravitational attraction of the Moon. Since tides dissipate the energy, the rotation of the Earth must have been continuously slowing down, and it was estimated that each day is longer than the previous one by two hundred millionths of a second. In spite of this small rate of increase, the cumulative effect becomes appreciable during long periods of time, and during one century the total discrepancy in clock-reading becomes fourteen seconds. This figure stands in good agreement with the discrepancy discovered in astronomical data by comparing today's observations with those carried out in the middle of the last century.

Since the rotation of the Earth slows down because of lunar tides, the law of conservation of angular momentum requires that the revolution of the Moon around the Earth must speed up, and its distance from us gradually increases; each time we see a new moon it is 10 cm further away. Dividing the present distance of the Moon by that rate of recession, one finds that the Moon and the Earth must have been quite close together about five thousand million years ago. Although the dispute is still going on about whether the Earth and the Moon were formerly one single body or whether they were formed independently as a twin body, there is no doubt that the date of five thousand million years ago corresponds to the formation of the Earth-Moon system as well as probably to the entire planetary system.

The Age of Stars in the Milky Way

We can now broaden our question, and ask about the age of stars forming our Milky Way system. As was mentioned in the previous chapter, one has to distinguish between two types of stellar populations: Population I, representing about a fifty-fifty mixture of stars and interstellar material; and Population II, formed entirely by stars. Since the processes of condensation of stars from interstellar material are apparently going on continuously in Population I, it does not represent a homogeneous age group, and contains extremely bright stars which must have been formed quite recently. On the other hand, there is every reason to believe that the stars of Population II were all formed at about the same time, early in the history of the Milky Way.

We now know that stellar energy is produced by thermonuclear reactions taking place in the hot stellar interior. The principal process in the stars of the main sequence is the transformation of hydrogen into helium, either through the formation of deuterium in the collision between two protons as in the Sun and the fainter stars or by the consecutive capture of four protons by the nucleus of carbon in brighter stars. The star remains on the main sequence as long as it has enough hydrogen in its central convective core, and wanders away into the region of Red Giants when the original hydrogen content is depleted. Since, according to mass-luminosity relation, the luminosity of stars increases as the cube of their mass (while the hydrogen supply is, of course, simply proportional to the mass), the life span of any given star decreases as the square of its mass. The main sequence of stars in Population II shows a sharp upper limit of luminosity corresponding to the stars with an expected life span between five and six thousand million years, from which one concludes that this figure must also represent the age of our Milky Way system. Thus, it seems that according to all available evidence, the Milky Way, including our Sun and its planets, must have been formed between five and six thousand million years ago.

Dispersal of Galaxies

In the early twenties the Mount Wilson astronomer, Edwin Hubble, made an astonishing discovery about the galaxies which populate the space of the Universe around us. He found that the lines in the spectra of distant galaxies are shifted towards the red end, and that this red shift increases with distance. Being interpreted in terms of Doppler effect, this observation meant that the galaxies are running away from us, and the farther they are, the faster they run. The detailed studies carried out by Hubble and his collaborator, M. L. Humason, led to the finding that the recession velocity v increases in direct proportion to the distance d, so that one can write

$$v = Hd \qquad (2.1)$$

where H is known as Hubble's constant. The distances used in the derivation of this formula were obtained by accepting the inverse square law for the visual brightnesses of distant galaxies, and most data pertained to clusters of galaxies for which more reliable average brightnesses could be used. It goes without saying that the observed recession of galaxies from the particular point of space where we are located does not mean the return to the Ptolomeic system in which we are located in the centre of the Universe. It is just a kind of optical illusion arising from the fact that all velocities are referred to our own galaxy. Imagine a rubber balloon with a number of spots painted more or less uniformly all over its surface. If we begin to inflate the balloon, making it larger and larger, all the distances between the painted spots will increase proportionally. But to an observer (an intelligent insect) located in one spot it will look as if all other spots are receding from it with velocities increasing with distance, since there is more rubber to stretch between more distant spots. Thus, there is no actual centre of expansion, or to put it another way, the centre of expansion is always there where you are. We deal simply with a uniform dispersion of the system of galaxies, or the uniform expansion of the space of the Universe.

If the system of galaxies continuously disperses, one should conclude that some time in the past all galaxies were squeezed together and the mean density of matter in space was much larger than at present. (We shall see later that the newly proposed theory of the Steady State Universe disputes this conclusion, but for the moment we will argue using the Evolutionary point of view). It is clear that time in the past where all the galaxies were tightly packed together is simply given by the inverse value of Hubble's constant. From his original studies, Hubble derived the value of

$$H = 250 \text{ km/sec per light year}$$

from which it followed that the era of the big squeeze of the Universe was 1·8 thousand million years ago. It is natural to consider that state as the beginning of the evolution of the Universe which finally brought it to its present state. As we have already mentioned in the previous chapter, the figure $1·8 \times 10^9$ years for the age of the Universe stood in contradiction to geological data according to which some rocks are three or more thousand million years old. We have also seen that change of the distance scale by Baade removed that contradiction, decreasing the value of Hubble's constant by a factor 2·5 and thus raising the age of the Universe to about five thousand million years. Subsequent studies increase still more the scale of intergalactic distances, and in his recent report to the Solvay Congress, J. H. Oort assumes

$$H = 23 \text{ km/sec per light year} = 2·1 \times 10^{-18} \text{ sec}^{-1}$$

bringing up the age of the Universe to 17×10^9 years.

Is Expansion Slowing Down?

We will now raise an important question about the future of the present expansion process. Will it be continued indefinitely, or is it slowing down, and will it ultimately stop and reverse itself? To answer this question, we have to compare the kinetic energy of expansion with the potential energy of gravity forces acting between the galaxies. If the former is larger, the expansion will never stop; in the opposite case it will stop and reverse the process. Consider a sphere (Fig. 2.1) which is large enough to contain so many galaxies that the distribution of matter within the sphere can be considered uniform. As galaxies disperse, this sphere becomes larger and larger and its radius R increases with the

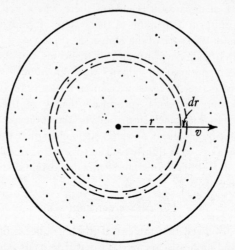

Fig. 2.1. Calculation of the kinetic energy of a spherical volume within the expanding Universe. (The dots represent individual galaxies)

speed $v = HR$ where H is Hubble's constant. The expansion velocities of the inner parts of the sphere with respect to its centre will be smaller in proportion to their distance from the centre, and will be given by rH. Since the mass of a shell with radius between r and $r + dr$ is $4\pi r^2 \rho dr$, ρ being the density, the total kinetic energy of the expanding sphere is

$$K = \int_0^R \tfrac{1}{2} 4\pi r^2 \rho \, (rH)^2 dr \;=\; \frac{2\pi}{5} \, \rho H^2 R^5 \qquad (2.2)$$

On the other hand, the gravitational energy of a sphere with uniform density is

$$U = -\frac{5}{3}\frac{GM^2}{R} = -\frac{16\pi^2}{15} \, G\rho^2 R^5 \qquad (2.3)$$

where G is the gravity constant. Dividing these two expressions we obtain

$$\frac{K}{|U|} = \frac{27H^2}{200\pi G\rho} \qquad (2.4)$$

which shows that the ratio of kinetic and potential energy is independent of the choice of radius of the sphere. Using for H the most recent value of Hubble's constant ($2 \cdot 1 \times 10^{-19}$ cm/sec per cm) and the value of the mean density of the Universe quoted at the end of the last chapter ($3 \cdot 10^{-31}$ g/cm³) one finds that, at the present time, kinetic energy of expansion exceeds the potential energy of gravitational attraction by a factor of about a thousand. This means that galaxies are essentially out of the grab of mutual gravity forces, so that the expansion is proceeding with a constant velocity and will never stop. This conclusion may be changed if future observations discover the presence of the so far undetected matter filling intergalactic space. Indeed if the amount of that matter exceeds by a factor of a thousand all the mass concentrated in galaxies, the value of ρ in the above formula will increase by that factor, K will become smaller than U, and the expansion will be bound to stop. The density of that hypothetical intergalactic material must be several thousand times smaller than the density of interstellar material within spiral arms. It can be said for certain that, if such material exists, it cannot have the same chemical constitution as interstellar clouds, which are formed 99 per cent of hydrogen and helium gases and about 1 per cent of dust. Even within our galaxy the dust causes the reddening, and at larger distances the total obscuration of stars, and the presence of dust in intergalactic space would make the observation of distant galaxies out of the question. The only possibility would be to assume that intergalactic space is filled up by pure hydrogen without any trace of dust. This assumption can be checked observationally, since this intergalactic hydrogen is expected to absorb the 21 cm wavelength in short radiowaves coming from very distant sources. The search for such absorption was recently made by G. B. Field, of Princeton University Observatory, with a negative result which indicates that if the hydrogen is present its density may not exceed $6 \cdot 10^{-29}$ g/cm³, which is several hundred times smaller than that necessary to stop the expansion. There remains, however, a loophole, since Field's results hold only under the assumption that about 90 per cent of that hydrogen is not ionized and thus effective in absorption. If the ionization is considerably higher, the presence of hydrogen may escape observation.

Another way of checking the possible slowing of the expansion is the observation of the red shift in the very distant galaxies. Indeed, because of the finite speed of light, we look far back in time when we look far out in space. If the expansion of the Universe is slowing down, the light which is reaching us from the distant galaxies must have been emitted when their recession speed was higher than it is now, and the observations must deviate from Hubble's linear relation between distance and the recession velocity. Observations in this direction were carried out several years ago by Humason for six clusters of galaxies, located about two thousand million years away. He found that these clusters of galaxies have higher recession velocities than expected from Hubble's relation. This result is subject, however, to the same objection as the old Hubble conclusion concerning the positive curvature of the space of the Universe. The light which comes from these galaxies started its travel two thousand million years ago and, if the galaxies become fainter with their age, the intensity was somewhat larger than that emitted by an average galaxy today. Introducing a corresponding correction in distance, we would place these galaxies somewhat farther away and they may fall on the regular Hubble line. Here again we are in trouble, because we do not know how the galaxies evolve in time.

CHAPTER 3

Evolutionary and Steady State Cosmologies

Static Universe

After the brilliant success of the General Theory of Relativity in its application to gravitational phenomena within our planetary system – i.e. the explanation of the precession of the perihelion of Mercury and the prediction of the deflection of light rays passing close to the Sun – Einstein made an attempt to use it for the description of the Universe as a whole. Since these attempts were made before Hubble's discovery of the red shift, at a time when it was believed that galaxies hang motionless in space, or possibly possess randomly distributed velocities, Einstein was looking for a static model of the Universe. As a result of this wishful thinking, he came to the conclusion that his basic equation of General Relativity, being applied to masses distributed uniformly through space, can possess only a solution which is independent of time, but that, in order to obtain such a solution, it is necessary to add to the basic equation an extra term containing the cosmological constant Λ. This led to the famous spherical model of the Universe in which a rocket travelling steadily in one direction would return to the origin from the opposite point on the sky. The cosmological term which Einstein added to his equation in order to obtain the desired effect can be interpreted physically as a repulsive force between the galaxies which increases proportionally to the distance between them. It goes without saying that such a force does not fit very well into the frame of all other physical forces which always decrease with distance, but there seemed to be no other way out. On the basis of that theory, Einstein derived a relation between the curvature radius of the Universe and the mean density of matter in it, a relation which did not fit observational data, leading to much too small a value of the curvature radius.

Another solution to Einstein's equation with the added cosmological term was obtained by the Dutch astronomer de Sitter and corresponded to a model of the Universe which is not only closed in space but also closed in time so that all events taking place in it would repeat periodically. However, de Sitter's solution could only be obtained on condition that either the density of matter in space is exactly zero (an empty

Universe) or that the matter filling it exerts a negative pressure. These inconsistencies and contradictions made both Einstein's and de Sitter's static models of the Universe rather unattractive and all the attempts to fit them to the actual Universe did not lead to any good result.

Friedman's Correction

At this difficult point in the history of cosmology there appeared a paper by a Russian mathematician, A. Friedman, in which he showed that Einstein made an algebraic mistake in his proof that only static solutions of the cosmological equation are mathematically possible and that, in fact, there must exist also dynamical solutions, one corresponding to an expanding and another to a contracting Universe. Friedman died soon after the publication of his paper, and further development of the theory was carried out by the Belgian astronomer G. Lemaitre, who applied it to the, at that time, newly discovered red shift in the spectra of the distant galaxies. The work of Lemaitre laid the foundation for the present evolutionary theory of the Universe. If the matter of the Universe is at present in a state of rapid expansion, it must have been in an extremely compressed state five or more thousand million years ago when the expansion had just started. Since compression is always connected with heating, primordial matter must have been in a state of uniform gas of extremely high temperature. As the expansion proceeded, primordial gas uniformly filling the space of the Universe was becoming rarer and cooler and at a certain era must have been broken up into giant gas clouds from which the present-day stellar galaxies developed. Thus, the problem of cosmogony is to study and to describe mathematically all the stages of that development from the early hot gas stage to the state of the Universe as we know it today.

It is interesting to notice that not only is that point of view accepted by the majority of astronomers, but it is also endorsed by the authority of the Church. In his '*Discourse*' published in 1953, Pope Pius XII writes

> If we look back into the past at the time required for this process of the 'Expand-ing Universe', it follows that, from one to ten thousand million years ago, the matter of the spiral nebular (galaxies) was compressed into a relatively restricted space, at the time the cosmic processes had their beginning . . . (At that time) the density, pressure and temperature of matter must have reached absolutely enormous proportions . . .

Steady State Hypothesis

Before Baade removed the discrepancy between the age of the Universe as estimated from the red shift, and from geological data, the mathematical astronomers T. Gold and H. Bondi from Cambridge University, later joined by F. Hoyle, introduced a new revolutionary hypothesis. According to that hypothesis, the dispersal of galaxies does not lead to increasing rarification of matter in the space of the Universe, since new matter is continuously created in intergalactic space at a rate which just compensates the result of expansion. From this newly created matter new galaxies are continuously formed, so that the total number of galaxies in a given volume of the Universe remains always the same. Thus, the Universe on the whole remains unchangeable from eternity in the past to eternity in the future. The philosophical foundation for such a hypothesis is the 'perfect cosmological principle' which states that, since the Universe looks the same no matter which part of space we inspect, it must look the same no matter when we look. As an immediate consequence of that assumption, one finds that the galaxies forming our Universe are not of the same age, as in the case of the Universe expanding from a singular compressed state, but represent a widespread age group, from very young ones, recently formed from newly created intergalactic matter, to very very old ones. Thus, one can always pick out of this display a galaxy which has exactly the age of our Milky Way system, as determined by the above-described method. The inverse Hubble's constant loses its meaning as determining the age of the Universe, but remains characteristic of the rate of creation of matter and of the mean age of the galaxies. Indeed, let us consider a large cubical volume in the Universe with the side l. According to Hubble's law the side of that cube increases at the rate

$$\frac{dl}{dt} = Hl \tag{3.1}$$

For the rate of change of the volume we have

$$\frac{1}{V}\frac{dV}{dt} = 3\frac{1}{l}\frac{dl}{dt} = 3H \tag{3.1}$$

If new matter is created at the rate $d\rho/dt$ which keeps the density constant, we must have

$$\frac{1}{\rho_0}\frac{d\rho}{dt} = \frac{1}{V}\frac{dV}{dt} = 3H \tag{3.3}$$

or

$$\frac{d\rho}{dt} = 3H\rho_0 \tag{3.4}$$

where ρ_0 is the constant density of the Universe.

Using $H = 2.1 \times 10^{-19}$ sec^{-1} and $\rho_0 = 3 \times 10^{-31}$ g/cm^3 we get

$$\frac{d\rho}{dt} = 1.9 \times 10^{-49} \text{ g/cm}^3 \text{ sec} \tag{3.5}$$

or 0.3 hydrogen atoms per cubic kilometre per century. Let us now calculate the average age of matter contained in the volume V. Since new matter is created at the rate given by the above formula, old matter must get out through the walls of the volume at the same rate, and the amount of 'old' matter which was created the time t ago must by now be reduced by a factor $exp\,(-3Ht)$. Thus for the average age of matter, we get

$$\overline{T} = \frac{\displaystyle\int_{-\infty}^{0} 3H\,\rho_0\,exp(-3Ht)\,dt}{\displaystyle\int_{-\infty}^{0} exp\,(-3Ht)\,dt} = \frac{1}{3H} \tag{3.6}$$

Since the time necessary for the condensation of galaxies from newly condensed matter can be assumed to be comparatively short, the above expression must also represent the average age of galaxies. Here lies the great difference between the Evolutionary and the Steady State theories. Whereas in the former $1/H$ represents the approximate age of all galaxies, in the latter the average age of the galaxies is given by one-third of that value, with a large scatter in both directions.

At the present time the decision between the Evolutionary and the Steady State theory lies essentially in obtaining more reliable observational material concerning individual galaxies, and clusters of galaxies, from which their ages can be estimated. Astronomers working on the galaxies in our neighbourhood, in which individual bright stars can be seen, seem to be of the opinion that they are all of the same age, which would contradict the Steady State theory. A recent publication by K. Just in which he studied the 'richness' of distant clusters of galaxies (i.e. the number of individual members in them) seems to indicate that the clusters located farther away, which we see now in the light emitted from them at the earliest era of the life of the Universe, show considerably lower 'richness' than the clusters located closer to us. If confirmed, this will be another piece of evidence against the Steady State theory, according to which large scale features of the Universe do not depend on time. But the evidence pro and contra is not absolutely conclusive, and the present situation is best characterized by the following Gallup Poll recently taken by the Science Service Agency in Washington, D.C.

Gallup Poll on Cosmology

Conducted by Science Service, Washington, D.C., in January, 1959.
The Grand Jury consisted of 33 astronomers from the United States and other countries.

Questions	Yes	No	No Comment
	%	%	%
Did the Universe start with a 'big bang' several thousand million years ago?	33·3	36·4	30·3
Is matter continuously created in space?	24·2	54·6	21·2
Will the disagreement between the Evolutionary and Steady State theories be resolved by A.D. 2000?	69·7	9·1	21·2
Will the answer be given by radio astronomy?	60·5	9·1	30·4
Will it be solved by a telescope on the satellite?	33·3	21·2	45·5
Is a Gallup Poll of this kind helpful to scientific progress?	0·0	100·0	0·0

Having worked on the Evolutionary theory of the Universe, and being more familiar with it than with the Steady State theory, I will put more weight on it and discuss in more detail its claims and conclusions.*

Mechanical Law of Expansion

In the previous chapter we derived the expression for the kinetic and potential energy of a spherical volume in the expanding Universe, and concluded that with the present mean density of the Universe, its kinetic energy of expansion is much larger than the potential energy of the forces of gravity, so that in the future our Universe is bound to expand beyond any limits. We want now to derive a formula connecting the rate of expansion with the changing density of the material which fills the Universe. All we have to state is that the sum of the kinetic and potential energy (i.e. $K + U$) of any part of the Universe remains constant in the process of expansion. Using the expressions derived in the previous chapter, we write

$$\frac{2\pi}{5} \rho H^2 R^5 - \frac{16}{15} \pi^2 G \rho^2 R^5 = \text{const } \rho R^3 \qquad (3.7)$$

which, by using Hubble's formula, can be reduced to

$$\frac{1}{R} \frac{dR}{dt} = \sqrt{\frac{8\pi G}{3} \rho - \frac{\text{const}}{R^2}} \qquad (3.8)$$

* See Chs. 9–13 by Dr. Thomas Gold for recent developments in the Steady State theory.

It is interesting to notice that the expression, derived here simply from the law of conservation of energy in Newtonian mechanics, is identical with that which can be obtained as the solution of the Cosmological equation of Einstein's General Theory of Relativity, and thus can safely be used in the study of the behaviour of the Expanding Universe. If we know how the density ρ depends on R, we can easily describe kinematical features of the Universe in the past and in the future.

Matter versus Radiation

In considering the behaviour of the mean density of the Universe during its expansion, one must remember that the ponderable material filling the space consists of two parts: *matter proper*, that is atoms, electrons, etc., and *radiant energy*, which is in thermal equilibrium with matter. Under ordinary conditions, as for example inside a room, the mass-density of radiant energy is negligibly small. According to the Stephan – Boltzmann formula the energy density at (absolute) temperature T is

$$\epsilon = aT^4 \text{ erg/cm}^3 \text{ where } a = 7 \cdot 6 \times 10^{-15} \tag{3.9}$$

which gives for the room temperature (about $300°K$) the value of about $6 \cdot 10^{-5}$ erg/cm^3. Dividing that figure by the square of the velocity of light, we get the mass density $7 \cdot 10^{-26}$ g/cm^3 which is, of course, negligibly small compared with the density (10^{-3} g/cm^3) of the atmospheric air. However, the situation is rather different if we ask ourselves about the balance between matter and radiation in the Universe as a whole. In fact, we have seen that the mean density of matter in the Universe is $3 \cdot 10^{-31}$ g/cm^3. If the temperature of the Universe is as low as $13°K$, the mass density of radiation becomes equal to the density of matter. If, as is possible, it is a few degrees above absolute zero, the mass density of radiation will be less than that of matter, but not by such a tremendous factor as in the example given above for the situation in a room.

Now let us compare heat capacities of matter and radiant energy in space. The heat capacity of gas is given by the familiar formula

$$C_{gas} = \tfrac{3}{2} k N \text{ erg/cm}^3 \text{ degree} \tag{3.10}$$

where $k = 1 \cdot 37 \times 10^{-16}$ is the Boltzmann constant, and N the number of particles per unit volume. For the density $3 \cdot 10^{-31}$ g/cm^3, N is $1 \cdot 5 \times 10^{-7}$ atoms/cm^3 (or one atom per five cubic meters), and we get

$$C_{gas} = 3 \cdot 4 \times 10^{-47} \text{ erg/cm}^3 \text{ degree} \tag{3.11}$$

On the other hand, the heat capacity of radiation is

$$C_{rad} = 4aT^3 = 3 \cdot 10^{-14} T^3 \text{ erg/cm}^3 \text{ degree} \tag{3.12}$$

which shows us that, even if the temperature of space is only a fraction of one degree absolute, the heat capacity of radiation is much larger than that of material gas. This result is of great importance for all considerations concerning the expansion of the Universe, since it shows that thermal balance during the expansion is maintained by radiation and not by matter.

Let us now consider the effect of expansion on the density of matter and radiation. Since matter is conserved, its density, that is the number of particles per cubic centimetre, will decrease inversely with the volume of the expanding region, i.e. as $1/R^3$ where R has the same meaning as in the earlier formulae. In the case of radiation, the situation is quite different, since radiant energy is spent in the expansion. The easiest way to visualize it is to consider a cube with the side R filled up with black body radiation of a certain temperature T. It will consist of standing waves of different lengths with the energy distribution given by Planck's formula. Now, if we begin to expand the volume adiabatically, all wavelengths will increase in proportion to R, and so also will the wave λ_{max} corresponding to maximum intensity in the spectrum. Remembering Wien's law for the black body radiation, we write

$$RT \sim \lambda_{max}T = \text{const} \tag{3.13}$$

which shows that in the process of expansion the temperature drops in inverse proportion to R. It follows now from the Stephan – Boltzmann law that *in the process of expansion the density of radiation will change in inverse proportion to R^4*, which is faster than the change of the density of gas. Thus, even though at the present time the mass of matter in the Universe may exceed the mass of the radiation, *at some time in past history radiation must have been gravitationally more important than matter*, and there must have been pounds or even tons of radiation per each ounce of matter. Due to the prevalence of radiation, matter, which is now condensed into stars and galaxies, must have been spread uniformly through space in the form of thin gas, the particles of which were being tossed to and fro by the impacts of light quanta.

Temperature Changes in the Early History of the Universe

We can now return to our equation (3.8) describing the time behaviour of the expanding Universe, and apply it to the early period when radiant energy was playing the prevailing role. We can neglect the density of matter as compared with the density of radiations and write, from (3.9)

$$\rho = \frac{aT^4}{c^2} \tag{3.14}$$

where c is the speed of light (mass energy equivalence).

We may also neglect the second term under the radical in (3.8) for small R, since it changes only as $1/R^2$, whereas the first term changes as $1/R^4$. Thus, the equation reduces to

$$\frac{1}{R}\frac{dR}{dt} = \sqrt{\frac{8\pi G}{3}\frac{aT^4}{c^2}} \qquad (3.15)$$

containing two functions of time: variable distance scale R and variable temperature T. Since, however, according to the previous argument, T is inversely proportional to R, we have

$$\frac{1}{R}\frac{dR}{dt} = -\frac{1}{T}\frac{dT}{dt} \qquad (3.16)$$

and our equation becomes

$$-\frac{1}{T}\frac{dT}{dt} = \sqrt{\frac{8\pi Ga}{3c^2}}\,T^2 \qquad (3.17)$$

This equation has a simple solution

$$T = \sqrt[4]{\frac{3c^2}{32\pi Ga}}\frac{1}{\sqrt{t}} = \frac{1\cdot5 \times 10^{10}\ {}^{\circ}K}{\sqrt{t}} \qquad (3.18)$$

where t is expressed in seconds and is counted from the beginning of expansion. It is very gratifying that the coefficient in the above formula is composed exclusively from universal constants (gravitational constant, velocity of light, and Stephan – Boltzmann constant) containing no arbitrary factors, and the formula is derived by using the law of conservation of energy and the basic law of black body radiation. Substituting the numerical values, we find that the Universe must have been a few thousand million degrees hot at the state of maximum contraction, cooling in the course of the first year to one million degrees and in the next million years to only three thousand degrees absolute.

The Origin of Elements

During the very early stages of the expansion of the Universe matter must have been completely dissociated into elementary particles, being a mixture of free electrons, protons and neutrons. As the temperature began to drop, neutrons and protons began to stick together, forming complex nuclei, such as deuterons, tritons, and the two isotopes of helium. G. Gamow investigated this aggregation process, using the above chart for the temperature and assuming various densities of matter at that time. His calculations were repeated in more detail by E. Fermi and A. Turkevich, with the results shown in Fig. 3.1. We notice that the entire process of aggregation occupies only about thirty minutes. At the end of this period nuclear reactions come to a standstill, partially because neutrons disappear as a result of natural decay and their capture by heavier nuclei, and partially because thermal velocities of protons become too low for penetration through the potential barriers. As a result of this aggregation, matter must have been composed, by the end of the process, of about 60 per cent of hydrogen, about 40 per cent of helium-4, and a few per cent of tritium and helium-3, which could be used as cornerstones for the building up of heavier elements.

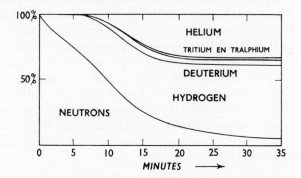

Fig. 3.1. Chemical composition of the Universe during the first thirty minutes of expansion

An attempt to study the further aggregation process was made by R. Alpher, H. Bethe, G. Gamow, and R. Herman. Using the smoothed out cross-sections for neutron capture in heavier elements, they were able to construct a theoretical abundance curve which stood in reasonably good agreement with the observed abundances. However, this theory ran into serious difficulty when the details of neutron capture processes were considered. Since no stable nucleus with atomic weight 5 exists, the next step beyond He^4 can be accomplished either by double neutron capture by helium-4

$$He_2^4 + 2N_0^1 \rightarrow He_2^6 + \text{radiation}$$
$$He_2^6 \rightarrow Li_3^6 + e-$$

(3.19)

or by more complex processes, such as

$$He_2^4 + H_1^3 \rightarrow Li_3^7 + \text{radiation}$$

(3.20)

The reaction rates of these processes are very low, leading to the calculated abundances of heavier elements being short by a factor of about one hundred. It does not seem that this difficulty caused by non-existence of mass 5 can be removed, and the present conclusion is that, while a small amount of heavy elements must have been produced during the early stages of expansion, the main bulk of them was synthesized later by some other process.

As will be discussed later, heavy elements can also be produced within ageing stars, and spread through interstellar space in the processes of supernovae explosions. This material can be accreted by the already existing stars, or condensed into new stars containing considerably larger concentrations of heavy elements than there were in the primordial Universe. The possibility is, indeed, not excluded that we have here the explanation of the existence of two types of stellar populations. The stars belonging to Population II are known to contain much smaller concentrations (by a factor of a hundred) of heavy elements than the stars of Population I. Thus, one can speculate that, while the stars of Population II are built from primordial material formed during the early stages of the Expanding Universe, the stars of Population I including our Sun, are, so to speak, 'secondhand stars' condensed from the remnants of other stars which have existed in a distant past and, having exploded, spread their material through interstellar space.

CHAPTER 4

Formation and Evolution of Galaxies

Transition Point

We have seen in the previous chapter that during the early stages of the expanding Universe the gravitational mass of thermal radiation was prevailing over the mass of ordinary matter, so that the rate of expansion was governed entirely by the former. However, as the expansion proceeded, a certain amount of radiant energy was continuously spent on the work against the forces of gravity, and at a certain era the mass density of radiation must have become first equal to and then smaller than that of matter. In order to estimate the time when that important event took place, we can proceed in the following fashion: substituting (3.18) into the Stephan – Boltzmann formula, and dividing by c^2, we get the following equation for the mass density of radiation during the early history of the Universe

$$\rho_{rad} = \frac{4 \cdot 3 \times 10^5}{t^2} \text{ g/cm}^3 \tag{4.1}$$

This dependence is represented in Fig. 4.1 by a continuous line marked 'radiation'. In logarithmic plot the line has the slope $-2 \cdot 0$. The encircled point in the lower right part of the diagram corresponds to the present time and to the present density of matter as it was derived in the first two chapters. Since at the present era the expansion proceeds uniformly, the density of matter decreases as the inverse cube of time, so that drawing through that point a line with the slope $-3 \cdot 0$ marked 'matter' we obtain the density of matter in the past. It is seen from Fig. 4.1 that the radiation and matter curves intersect at a point corresponding to one-tenth of the present age of the Universe, which brings us to the conclusion that, whereas radiation was prevailing during the first 10 per cent of the history of the Universe, matter is prevailing during the last 90 per cent. It must be remarked here that the position of the intersection point is very sensitive to the accepted numerical values of the present age and the present mean density of the Universe. Since both these values are at present subject to great uncertainty, the position of the intersection shown in Fig. 4.1 should also be considered as only very approximate.

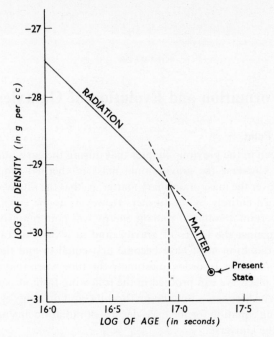

Fig. 4.1. Changes of radiation and matter densities in various stages of the expanding Universe

Gravitational Instability

When, in its continuous development, the expanding Universe passed through the critical point discussed above, and the gravitational influence of matter became larger than that of radiation, something very important must have happened. Many years ago Sir James Jeans showed that gravitating gas uniformly filling a sufficiently large volume is intrinsically unstable, and is bound to break up into individual gas spheres of a certain radius. Jeans's argument can be reproduced in a simplified way as follows. Consider a large body of gas with the density ρ and temperature T. Due to various causes, and in particular to the turbulence which is always expected to exist in such cases, fluctuations of gas density in various regions must be taking place. If the increase of density takes place in a comparatively small region, the increased gas pressure tending to dissolve it will do its job, and the local condensation will disappear. If, however, the size of the condensation region is sufficiently large, gravitational forces between different parts of gas will take the upper hand over the gas pressure, and, instead of dispersing, the rudimental condensation will continue to grow. The condition for the stability of rudimentary concentration is that gravitational forces due to its mass prevent individual gas particles from escaping from its surface. If the radius of condensation is R, the gravitational potential on its surface is

$$\frac{GM}{R} = \frac{4}{3}\frac{\pi GR^3 \rho}{R} = \frac{4\pi G}{3}\rho\, R^2 \tag{4.2}$$

where G is the constant of gravity. On the other hand, the kinetic energy of gas particles at the temperature T is $\frac{3}{2}kT$, k being Boltzmann's constant. Thus, the condition under which gas particles cannot escape from the surface of the condensation is

$$\frac{4\pi\, G\rho R^2\, m}{3} > \frac{3}{2}k\, T \tag{4.3}$$

m being the mass of the particles. The above condition can be written as

$$R > \sqrt{\frac{9k}{4\pi\, Gm}\frac{T}{\rho}} \tag{4.4}$$

or, putting in numerical values, and assuming the gas to be hydrogen

$$R > 3{\cdot}10^7 \sqrt{\frac{T}{\rho}}\,\text{cm} \tag{4.5}$$

If we apply this condition to the atmospheric air, with T about $300°$K and ρ about 10^{-3} g/cm^3, we obtain $R > 1{\cdot}5 \times 10^{10}$ cm $= 150,000$ km as the minimum size of the condensation which can be held by gravitational forces. The fact that this figure is considerably larger than the thickness of the terrestrial atmosphere explains why atmospheric air does not break up into a number of gas spheres with a vacuum between them. The situation is, however, quite different in the case of infinite expanses of gas where the condensations of any radius are possible.

At the critical point at which matter became gravitationally more important than radiation, the gas which was heretofore uniformly distributed through space must have become gravitationally unstable, with the tendency to break up into individual giant gas spheres. As we see from Fig. 4.1, the density at that point must have been about $3{\cdot}10^{-30}$ g/cm^3, and the temperature formula derived in the previous section gives $T = 50°$ K. For that temperature and density Jeans's formula gives

$$R > 10^{23}\,\text{cm} = 100,000\,\text{light years}$$

which is the correct order of magnitude for the sizes of the galaxies.

Calculating the mass contained in that volume, we arrive at

$$M > 10^{40} \text{ g} = 10^{17} \text{ sun masses}$$

which stands in agreement with the smallest observed galactic masses.

The agreement between the values calculated from the theory and those obtained observationally is, of course, only very rough. As mentioned previously, the results of theoretical calculations are very sensitive to the accepted values of the present age and density of the Universe, which are far from being rigidly established and can easily change in either direction because of future observations. Nevertheless, it is gratifying that the sizes and masses of galaxies obtained from the theory fall within the observed limits while *a priori* they could be wrong by a factor of a million in either direction.

The Role of Turbulence

As was mentioned before, the primordial gas filling the space of the Universe must have been in a state of violent turbulent motion. In fact, turbulence is a natural state of large bodies of liquids and gases, be they rivers, oceans, the atmosphere, or the gaseous nebula. Studies of turbulent flow of fluid in pipes show that the smooth 'laminar' flow breaks up into irregular 'turbulent' motion when a certain relation between the velocity of the fluid, its vicsosity, its density, and the diameter of the pipe is satisfied. In fact, one finds that turbulence always occurs when the so-called Reynolds number, defined as

$$R = \frac{(\text{velocity}) \times (\text{density}) \times (\text{diameter})}{(\text{viscosity})} \tag{4.6}$$

becomes larger than 1000. Thus, for the same fluid moving through pipes of different diameters, turbulence will occur at lower velocities in a pipe of a larger diameter. For the motions within an unlimited body of fluid, such as in the atmospheric air or in the gaseous nebulae, the diameter of the pipe can be taken to be infinite, so that turbulence is expected to take place no matter how slowly the fluid moves. We can see turbulent motion on the surface of a fast-flowing river when we look down from the bridge, and we can feel it in the form of a discontinuous gust of the wind blowing in our faces.

Turbulence in a fluid medium is a very complicated and completely orderless motion, which is not easy to represent by a simple picture or a diagram. Probably the nearest representation of what turbulence actually is, is given by Fig. 4.2, in which individual turbulent streamers are represented schematically by arrows of different sizes. If we look at this diagram from a distance we first observe large arrows winding around one another. Closer inspection will show, however, that the large arrows consist of a large number of smaller ones which in turn consist of arrows of still smaller size. Extend this picture in both directions so that the largest arrows will be almost as large as the entire volume of the fluid, and the smallest ones almost as small as intermolecular distances, and you will have a fairly clear picture of what turbulent motion actually is. The verse by L. F. Richardson neatly describes it

> 'Big whirls have little whirls,
> That feed on their velocity;
> And little whirls have lesser whirls,
> And so on to viscosity.'

The last line refers to the fact that the energy of turbulent motion continuously passes from larger whirls which can easily be seen by the eye, to smaller and smaller ones, and finally goes over into thermal motion through the viscous friction of the fluid.

In Fig. 4.2 the arrows in each category are shown as being about the same size, for convenience in drawing. In actuality, the hierarchy of

Fig. 4.2. Eddies of different orders in a homogeneous turbulent motion

turbulent streamers includes all sizes of arrows as well as all directions of motion. Turbulent motion within a fluid includes the rotational as well as transitory motions of different elements, and it is because of this rotational type of motion that turbulent streamers are commonly known as 'eddies'. It would be incorrect to think that turbulent eddies maintain their individuality for a long time, enabling us to represent turbulent motion by giving the position of different eddies for properly chosen intervals of time. Actually, the lives of individual eddies are very short, and they usually fade out and disappear after travelling a distance comparable with their size, giving rise to new eddies which may move in an entirely different direction.

At first glance, it would seem impossible to develop a consistent theory of such a complex and irregular motion as that presented by a turbulent flow, and until recently the study of turbulence was carried out, mostly by engineers, on a purely empirical basis. But during recent years the theory of turbulence was put on a strict mathematical basis, by the work of Sir G. Taylor in England, Th. von Karman in the U.S.A., W. Heisenberg and Ch. von Weizsacker in Germany, and A. N. Kolmogoroff in Russia. One of the main results of that research was the derivation of the 'energy spectrum' of turbulent motion. The motion of eddies involves large amounts of kinetic energy, which is being continuously transferred from larger eddies to smaller ones, all the way down from the large-scale motion to the thermal motion of molecules. The question to be asked here is: how much energy is stored in eddies of different sizes? (i.e. what is their energy spectrum?). Theoretical considerations lead to the conclusion that the velocity distribution between the eddies of different sizes is governed by the so-called Kolmogoroff Law which can be written as

$$\text{(velocity)} \sim \sqrt[3]{\text{(size)}} \qquad (4.6)$$

In other words, the smaller the eddy, the smaller the velocity of the flow forming it. This law was found to describe quite correctly the observed velocity distribution in the gaseous nebulae of the Milky Way.

The existence of turbulent motion in the primordial gas of the expanding Universe is of paramount importance for the understanding of its break-up into individual clouds. Indeed, as we have seen before, the kinetic energy of expansion within any spherical volume within the expanding Universe is many times larger than the potential energy of gravity forces. Thus, if one assumes a complete homogeneity of the primordial gas, gravity forces could not possibly overcome the expansion inertia, and no condensations could have been formed. On the other hand, turbulent eddies in the expanding gas, causing large local increases in density, could easily lead to the condensations which satisfy Jeans's condition, and thus give rise to stable gas spheres of a size and mass compatible with those of the galaxies.

These protogalaxies, formed as a result of gravitational instability of primordial gas, must have retained the original characteristics of the turbulent eddies which were responsible for their existence. They must have been rotating at various speeds around randomly oriented axes, and also possessing a randomly distributed translatory motion. This is exactly what we observe now in the case of individual galaxies.

From Protogalaxies to Stellar Galaxies

When protogalaxies were first formed from primordial expanding gas, by the process just described, they were just giant clouds of cool gas drifting away from one another as a result of initial expansion, and gradually contracting as a result of gravity and rapidly dropping temperature. But, within their giant bodies Jeans's instability principle continued to work, and the secondary condensations into thousands of millions of smaller gas spheres were bound to take place. These secondary condensations, the 'protostars', which were originally also very dilute and quite cold, continued to contract, becoming denser and hotter, and within a few hundred million years turned into very hot and luminous bodies. When this process was completed, the original cool and dark gas masses of protogalaxies were transformed into the familiar swarms of shining stars.

But even though this transformation of the original dark protogalaxies of the past into the shining stellar galaxies of today took place thousands of millions of years ago, the galaxies still retain indications of their early youth. In fact, without the assumption that once upon a time galaxies were made entirely of gas, there would be no explanation of their present regular shapes of rotating fluid bodies.

The stars forming the galaxies of today are scattered through space so thinly that there is hardly any chance for them to influence one another's motion. It has been calculated that during the entire lifetime of a galaxy there could have been only a very few cases of two stars passing close enough to be appreciably deflected from their original tracks by the forces of mutual gravitational attraction. Under such circumstances the swarms of stars forming the galaxies could never have assumed regular ellipsoidal shapes, and would have remained shapeless and irregular star clouds for ever. The fact that, with very few exceptions such as the two Magellanic clouds, galaxies do possess the regular shapes of rotating fluid bodies can be understood only on the assumption that these galactic shapes originated while the galaxies were still in the gaseous state, and that the general configuration was not changed by the condensation of the gas masses into stars. We may refer to them as 'fossilized galactic shapes' by analogy with a geological fossil, such as petrified wood, which retains the exact shape and structure of a living organism although inorganic compounds were substituted for the original material a long time ago.

CHAPTER 5

Stars, Planets, and Life

Early Stages of Stellar Evolution

As we have seen in the previous chapter, stars must have condensed from the material of the original protogalaxies as a result of gravitational instability of gaseous masses. One can calculate that the process of the contraction of the original dilute protostars into dense bodies as we know them today must have taken about 10^8 years, a short period as compared with the total evolutionary scale of the Universe. Since the original gaseous material of protogalaxies must have been in a state of turbulent motion, protostars, besides participating in the large-scale rotational motion of the galaxies, must also have had randomly distributed velocities of their own, as well as various amounts of angular momenta. The presence of angular momenta accounts for the fact that a large proportion of protostars condensed into two, and sometimes three or more, separate bodies, forming double and multiple star systems. In the case of eddies with comparatively small angular momenta, almost all original material of protostars must have condensed in the centre leaving, however, a thin disc-shaped ring which later broke up into individual planets. According to G. P. Kuiper, about 1 per cent of all the stars within the galaxy must have acquired planetary systems.

When the body of the star was slowly contracting from the original dilute cool state, the temperature in its interior was rising higher and higher until at a certain stage it reached a value sufficiently high to kindle nuclear reactions between deuterium nuclei which must have been present in a certain amount in the primordial material. The reactions which must have started first

$$H_1^1 + H_1^2 \rightarrow He_2^3$$
$$He_2^3 + He_2^3 \rightarrow He_2^4 + 2 H_1^1 \tag{5.1}$$

were producing a sufficient amount of energy to put a stop for a while to the process of gravitational contraction, and to stabilize the stars as long as the deuterium supply lasted. When the deuterium was all used up, contraction proceeded until the central temperature reached the higher value necessary for the

$$Li_3^7 + H_1^1 \rightarrow 2 He_2^4 \tag{5.2}$$

reaction. Similarly, during the later contraction stages beryllium and boron were burned. Since the aforementioned elements were presumably present in very small amounts, the corresponding interruptions of the original contractive process were of comparatively short duration.

Main Sequence Stage

At a certain stage of contraction, the central temperature of the star reached the value of about twenty million degrees at which two important thermonuclear reactions begin to operate at a sufficiently high rate. One is the *carbon cycle* consisting essentially of a consecutive capture of four protons by a carbon nucleus, and their subsequent union into an alpha particle. In more detail, the reactions participating in the carbon cycle are

$$C_6^{12} + H_1^1 \rightarrow N_7^{13} + \text{radiation}$$
$$N_7^{13} \rightarrow C_6^{13} + e^+$$
$$C_6^{13} + H_1^1 \rightarrow N_7^{14} + \text{radiation}$$
$$N_7^{14} + H_1^1 \rightarrow O_6^{15} + \text{radiation}$$
$$O_6^{15} \rightarrow N_7^{15} + e^-$$
$$N_7^{15} + H_1^1 \rightarrow C_6^{12} + He_2^4 \tag{5.3}$$

Another important nuclear process taking place at about the same temperature is the $H - H$ reaction series

$$H_1^1 + H_1^1 \rightarrow H_1^2 + e^+$$
$$H_1^1 + H_1^2 \rightarrow He_2^3$$
$$He_2^3 + He_2^3 \rightarrow He_2^4 + 2 H_1^1 \tag{5.4}$$

Both reactions result in the transformation of hydrogen into helium, and, since hydrogen constitutes more than half of the material of the Universe, stars became stabilized for a very long period of time when the hydrogen-burning state was reached. The luminosity of the star inside which hydrogen is being transformed into helium depends on its central temperature which, in its turn, depends on the mass of the star. One can calculate, on the basis of a stellar model, that the luminosity of a star is proportional to the cube of its mass, which stands in good agreement with the empirical mass luminosity relation. Since the surface temperature also increases with the mass, stars of different masses are distributed along a narrow band known as the Main Sequence in the Russell-Hertzsprung diagram which is a graph in which the brightnesses of stars are plotted against their surface temperatures.

A remark must be made about the relative importance of the carbon cycle and $H - H$ reaction in stars of different masses. From the theoretical formulae for the reaction rates, one concludes that the former is much more sensitive to temperature than the latter, and that, in the case of the Sun, the H — H reaction is faster than the carbon cycle by a factor of about 10. Thus, our Sun and all the fainter stars, which form the majority of the stellar population, use H — H reaction for their energy production, while the stars brighter than the Sun, such as Sirius, use the carbon cycle.

Shell Source and Red Giants

In the evolutionary development of a star a very important role is played by the convective currents surrounding the central source of nuclear energy. Convective currents always originate in compressible fluids when the gradient of the temperature becomes large enough, and, in the point-source model of a star, temperature increases very sharply towards the centre. As a result, about 10 per cent of the stellar material surrounding the energy source is in a state of convection, and the convective currents in this region produce a continuous mixing, bringing fresh hydrogen into the reaction zone and removing helium produced in the reaction. On the other hand, no convection takes place in the outer envelope containing the remaining 90 per cent of the mass, and the heat transfer towards the surface is accomplished by the diffusion of light quanta through the highly ionized material. Under such circumstances, concentration of hydrogen in the convective zone gradually drops down, while hydrogen in the envelope remains intact. When hydrogen in the convective zone is nearly exhausted, the site of thermonuclear reactions moves from the centre of the star to the base of the hydrogen-rich envelope and the thermonuclear reaction zone begins to spread through that envelope as does a ring of fire caused by a match carelessly dropped in the middle of a field of dry grass. It can be shown that, as a result of the formation and expansion of that 'shell source' within the star, its radius begins to grow larger and larger while its surface temperature drops down. In spite of the decreasing emissivity per unit surface, the luminosity of the star goes up because of the rapid increase of its total surface. Thus, the star which developed a shell source becomes a red giant, such as Betelgeuse, Scheat, Ras Algethi, and other bright red stars.

While during the red giant stage of stellar evolution the radius of a star becomes hundreds and thousands of times larger than it was during the Main Sequence stage, the size of the helium core inside the shell source becomes smaller and smaller. The decrease in the geometrical dimensions of the core, combined with the steady increase of its mass, results in a rapidly rising density of helium from which it is composed. During this stage of evolution, new thermonuclear reactions originate in the centre of the core. Dr. E. Salpeter has shown that, under the conditions of very high density existing in the helium core of red giants, triple collisions of helium nuclei become of importance. The reaction is

$$\text{He}_2^4 + \text{He}_2^4 + \text{He}_2^4 \rightarrow \text{C}_6^{12} + \text{radiation} \tag{5.5}$$

This reaction is facilitated by the fact that, although two helium nuclei do not form a stable combination, which would be Be_4^8, they stick together for a sufficiently long time to give a chance for the third helium nucleus to come in, forming a stable C_6^{12} nucleus. This reaction is followed by other He_2^4 capture reactions

$$\text{C}_6^{12} + \text{He}_2^4 \rightarrow \text{O}_8^{16} + \text{energy}$$
$$\text{O}_8^{16} + \text{He}_2^4 \rightarrow \text{Ne}_{10}^{20} + \text{energy} \tag{5.6}$$

which lead gradually to the formation of heavier and heavier elements until the iron-chromium-nickel group is reached. Since the nuclei of these elements are most stable, corresponding to the minimum of the packing-fraction curve, no heavier elements can be built by regular thermonuclear processes. Thus, the formation of heavier elements up to uranium must be ascribed to some processes involving the capture of neutrons liberated in one way or another in the stellar interior. According to the views of F. Hoyle, W. Fowler and the Burbages, the formation of heavy elements takes place during the latest stage of the stellar evolution, when the star blows up in a spectacular show of a Supernova explosion. The material thrown out in the explosion mixes with the previously existing interstellar matter and enriches it with the heavy elements formed in the exploded star. This theory may explain the fact that, whereas the stars belonging to Population II contain only very small amounts of heavy elements, the stars of Population I, including our Sun, contain much larger amounts.

Planetary Systems

The earliest opinion on the subject of the origin and evolution of our planetary system was expressed in 1749 by Count de Buffon, who suggested that planets were formed as a result of a collision between our Sun and a comet. Several decades later, Immanuel Kant and the Marquis de Laplace proposed independently a much more reasonable theory according to which the planets were formed from a gaseous disc which resulted from the contraction of the primordial masses into the body of the Sun. Kant–Laplace views were severely criticized at the end of the nineteenth century by James Clerk Maxwell, who showed that, if the material now forming the planets had been distributed uniformly through the plane of ecliptics, gravitational forces would not have been strong enough to condense it back into the planets. Maxwell proved that such a condensation could not have taken place unless the total mass of the gaseous ring was about a hundred times larger than the combined mass of all the planets. Maxwell's calculations, which seemingly disproved the Kant–Laplace cosmogonical hypothesis, led to a complete turnover in the theory of the origin of the planetary system. Sir James Jeans in England, and Thomas C. Chamberlain and Forest Ray Moulton in the United States proposed the return to Buffon's collision theory, replacing the comet by a star which must have collided, or at least passed sufficiently close to the Sun. In such a close passage, gravitational forces between the two bodies could have extracted a filament of gaseous matter which would later have contracted into the individual planets. However, the collision theory of the origin of the planetary system had run into a series of serious difficulties, in particular in the attempt to explain the fact that planetary orbits are very nearly circular. The difficulties were piling up until, at the very end of World War II, another flip-over in planetary cosmogeny took place. In 1944 a German physicist, Karl von Weizsacker, indicated that Maxwell's objections to the original Kant–Laplace hypothesis do not hold any more in view of the new knowledge concerning the chemical constitution of the Universe. While in olden times it was believed that the constitution of our Earth, formed mostly by oxygen, silicon, and iron, is typical for the entire Universe, it was later found that stars and interstellar material are formed 99 per cent of a hydrogen–helium mixture with only about 1 per cent of the Earth-type material. This finding had completely changed the assumptions made by Maxwell in his analysis. Apparently the original ring around the Sun was about a hundred times heavier because of the overabundance of hydrogen and helium. Because of this much larger mass, gravitational forces acting between different parts of the ring were also much greater, and condensation of the ring material into planets could easily take place. But the original condensations, known as 'protoplanets,' must have been much larger than the planets as we know them today, consisting mostly of a hydrogen – helium mixture with only about 1 per cent of terrestrial elements.

Soon after the protoplanets were formed, the original interstellar dust, consisting of the particles of iron oxides, silicates, etc., settled towards their central regions, forming solid cores surrounded by huge hydrogen – helium atmospheres. It seems very likely that this process took place before the Sun itself had condensed sufficiently to become hot and luminous. When, millions of years later, the Sun became what it is now, the radiation pressure of the light emitted by it began to blow off the hydrogen – helium envelopes of the planets, and for a long period of time the planetary system must have looked like a family of giant comets with luminous tails of hydrogen – helium mixture being blown away into the surrounding space. In the case of inner planets, which include Mercury, Venus, Earth and Mars, radiation pressure of the sunrays was strong enough to blow off the entire gaseous atmosphere, exposing the rocky central cores. In the case of outer planets (Jupiter and beyond) the radiation pressure was weaker, and a considerable part of the original hydrogen – helium atmosphere was left over. This accounts for the fact that the observed mean density of outer planets is considerably lower than that of inner planets.

The Origin of Life

As I have mentioned before, today's cosmogonies suggest that one out of a hundred stars must have a planetary system similar to that of our Sun. Since the Milky Way contains about one hundred thousand million stars, we must conclude that there are within it about a thousand million planetary systems similar to our own. What are the chances that life similar to ours exists in those distant planetary systems? To answer this question, we must first ask ourselves how did life originate on the Earth.

We know that the most important substances forming living organisms are the proteins, the molecules of which are formed by very long chains of comparatively simple chemical compounds called amino acids. There are twenty different amino acids participating in the structure of proteins, and the order in which they are arranged into the sequence determines whether the protein will be active in regulating sugar content (insulin), catalizing the production of milk in an expectant mother (oxytocine), or coagulating blood streaming from an open wound (thromboplastin, prothrombin, and fibrinogen). Thus, to understand the origin of life, we must first understand the origin of amino acids on the barren young Earth. An organic chemist can easily synthesize any number of amino acids in his laboratory, and even unite them into the simplest protein molecules, but our problem is to find out how amino acids could originate in the natural way during the early stages of the existence of our planet.

The solution of this problem was suggested several years ago by an American chemist, Harold Urey. He indicated that the primordial atmosphere of the Earth must have been entirely different from what it is now. While the present terrestrial atmosphere is characterized by a large preponderance of oxygen, which is produced by vegetation covering the surface of our planet, the primordial atmosphere must have con-

tained a large amount of free hydrogen along with its compounds, and
such comparatively abundant elements as carbon, nitrogen, and oxygen
(i.e. hydrocarbon, ammonia, and water-vapour). The difference between
the constitution of the primordial and the present atmospheres of the
Earth is shown graphically in Fig. 5.1.

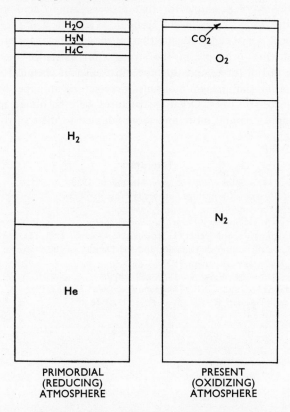

Fig. 5.1. The change of terrestrial atmosphere according to H. Urey

According to Urey's hypothesis, amino acids necessary for making
protein molecules could have originated from gases forming that primordial atmosphere under the action of the ultraviolet radiation of the Sun.
Urey's idea was soon confirmed by his student S. L. Miller who proved
experimentally that a mixture of methane (CH_4), ammonia (NH_3), and
water-vapour (H_2O), subjected to a slow electric discharge (equivalent
to ultraviolet) produces small amounts of amino acids found in proteins.
These amino acids, which presumably originated in the outer reaches of
the primordial atmosphere, have slowly descended to the ground level

(as the fission products do now) and, being dissolved in the ocean waters, formed an organic 'brew', the first step in the development of life.

Of course, it is a large step from the water solution of amino acids to the simplest living organism, and we still do not know how to close that gap. One can visualize, however, that during several thousand million years which were available for that process, amino acid molecules, uniting into long chains, went through a complicated evolutionary development. Once can speculate that, at these early stages of development, Darwin's principle of the struggle for existence was already operating in full force, and that the most efficient chemical reactions between primordial protein molecules were getting an upper hand over the less successful ones. Organic structures were becoming more and more complicated and more and more adapted to their surroundings. And so here we are!

Literature

Gamow, G., *The Creation of the Universe*. Macmillan, 1952.

Bondi, H., *Cosmology*, Cambridge University Press, 1952.

'The Universe' (a symposium), *Scientific American*, ——, Sept., 1956.

'Cosmogony' (by G. Gamow), *Encyclopaedia Britannica*.

Belzer, J., Gamow, G., and Keller G., *Astrophysical Journal*, 1951, **113**, 166.

Oort, J. H., 'Distribution of Galaxies and the Density of the Universe', *Onzieme Conseil de Physique*, Bruxelles, 1958.

Field, G. B., *Astrophysical Journal*, 1959, **129**, 536.

'Discorso di Sua Santita Pio XII', *Tipografia Poliglotta Vaticana*, 1953.

Alpher, R., and Herman, R., *Rev. Mod. Phys.*, 1950, **22**, 153.

CHAPTER 6

The Evolution of Stars and Star Clusters

Every star that we see at night is a gaseous sun. Some of these sun-stars are bodies very much larger than our own Sun and they shine with far greater intrinsic brilliance, whereas others are smaller and intrinsically much fainter than our own Sun. The Sun is pretty much a run-of-the-mill star, neither very bright nor very faint, neither very hot nor very cool, neither of very high nor of very low mass.

The disparity in intrinsic brightnesses of the stars first became apparent towards the end of the nineteenth century. Already, a little earlier, it had been found that stars of different colour show very different spectral characteristics, thus suggesting a wide spread in surface temperatures for the stars at large.

Observations of double stars, or 'binaries', gave the first evidence relating to stellar masses, with the surprising result that the range of stellar masses appeared much smaller than the observed range of intrinsic stellar luminosities. One of the major tasks of astronomers during the first twenty-five years of this century was that of sorting the stars according to their masses, intrinsic luminosities and surface temperatures, thus establishing the basic observed relations to be accounted for by future theories of stellar evolution.

Early in the present century Miss Antonia Maury of Harvard Observatory noted that some few stars showed unusually sharp absorption lines in their spectra. The Danish astronomer Ejnar Hertzsprung found soon afterwards that Miss Maury's sharp-line stars were all intrinsically very luminous, and it was apparently Hertzsprung again who first suggested that there might be 'giant' stars and 'dwarf' stars among those of each given spectral variety.

At about the same time the trigonometric measurements of stellar distances were becoming more plentifully available and the sorting according to spectral type and intrinsic brightness could proceed. By 1913–14, sufficient observational material had accumulated to permit Henry Norris Russell of Princeton Observatory to plot the famous diagram shown in Fig. 6.1, which, for obvious reasons, is now generally referred to as the Hertzsprung-Russell diagram, the H–R Diagram for short.

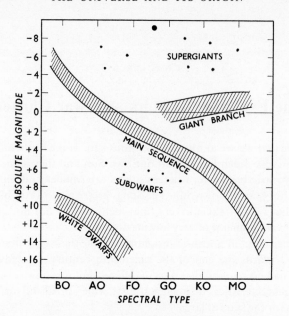

Fig. 6.1. The conventional Hertzsprung–Russell diagram for the region near the Sun (Population I)

Since the H-R Diagram plays a very fundamental role in all considerations of stellar evolution, it pays us to examine it in some detail. Horizontally, we find plotted the spectral types of the stars. The principal spectral classes that are considered at the present time are: O, B, A, F, G, K and M. There are others, but these need not concern us at the present time. The O and B stars have surface temperatures of the order of 20,000°K and greater; their spectra show absorption lines of some several times ionized atoms, such as difficult to excite helium, and rather weak Balmer lines of neutral hydrogen.

The A stars have surface temperatures around the 10,000°K mark, and in their spectra the Balmer lines of hydrogen are the predominant feature. The F and G stars are a bit on the cooler side, with surface temperatures of the order of 8000° and 6000°K, and their spectra show, along with relatively weak Balmer lines of hydrogen, fairly strong metallic lines and conspicuous lines of the rather easily ionized calcium atom. The coolest observed stars are the K and M stars, toward the right in the diagram, which have surface temperatures ranging from 4500° to 2500°K, and in which absorption lines from neutral atoms predominate, along with molecular bands. A good many astronomers have become adept at precise classification of stellar spectra and each of the major spectral divisions is often subdivided, sometimes in as many as ten subclasses.

Thus we speak of stars of spectral class B0, B1, B2, B3, B5, B8 and B9, where a star of spectral class B9 is not very different from one of spectral class A0. From left to right in the H–R Diagram, we proceed therefore from higher to lower temperatures, and the H–R Diagram is often plotted with a horizontal scale in which the spectral type is replaced by the inverse of the surface temperature.

Vertically we plot the so-called absolute magnitude. It is a derived quantity based upon the star's observed apparent magnitude and its distance, which three quantities are related by the basic formula

$$M = m + 5 - 5 \log d$$

According to ancient astronomical tradition, the apparent magnitudes, m, are measured on a logarithmic scale, with the brighter visible stars assigned zero and first apparent magnitude, and the faintest visible to the naked eye of the sixth apparent magnitude. To be precise, a difference of 5 in apparent magnitude corresponds to a ratio of apparent brightnesses of 100. A star of apparent magnitude $m = 21$ (now within reach of all major telescopes) has an apparent brightness equivalent to 1/100,000,000th part of the brightness of a first magnitude star.

Astronomers measure their distances professionally in 'parsecs', and for popular presentation the 'light year' is in vogue. The parsec is the distance of a star for which the measured trigonometric parallax would be equal to one second of arc, whereas the light year represents the distance covered by a light ray in one year; one parsec equals 3·258 light years. The simple basic relation that we have given above is equivalent to the inverse square law in terms of apparent and absolute magnitude scales. The absolute magnitude, M, is on the same logarithmic basis as the apparent magnitudes, with the understanding that the unit distance at which absolute magnitude is defined is equal to 10 parsecs.

We note immediately from Fig. 6.1 that the observed range of absolute magnitudes of the stars is very large indeed. There is a difference of absolute magnitude of almost twenty five magnitudes between the brightest and the faintest stars. We note that it would take 10^{10} stars of absolute magnitude $M = + 17$ to obtain the equivalent brightness of one star of $M = -8$. Our Sun is a 'Main Sequence' star of spectral class G0 and absolute magnitude $M = +5$.

For the vicinity of the Sun, the great majority of stars fall very close to the Main Sequence in the H–R Diagram. Most spectral types are also represented by a few conspicuous very luminous specimens, the giants and the supergiants, which per unit volume in space are very rare, but which can be observed at great distances simply because they are so luminous. Finally there are the modest 'subdwarfs' and the intrinsically very faint 'white dwarfs'. It is the function of a successful theory of stellar evolution to explain why there are these separate branches to the H–R Diagram and how we may understand the relative frequencies of the various types. We shall see below that the subdwarfs and the white dwarfs probably belong to what are known as Population II stars.

In the early 1920s the second basic relation came to light: the Mass – Luminosity Relation. Arthur Stanley Eddington discovered for the stars in the vicinity of the Sun that the absolute magnitude appears to be a single-valued function of the star's mass. But, whereas the range in intrinsic brightnesses as observed amounts to 10^{10}, the observed range of stellar masses amounts only to one thousand. The intrinsically faintest known stars seem to have masses of the order of one tenth of that of the Sun, sometimes a little less, whereas the most luminous supergiants do not appear to have masses in excess of one hundred times that of the Sun.

Stars have no machinery inside for permanent storage of energy, and the observed intrinsic brightness of a star is therefore a measure of the amount of atomic energy that is produced inside the star. We conclude quite simply that in a supergiant with a mass one hundred times that of the Sun, and with an intrinsic brightness one hundred thousand times that of the Sun, the internal atomic energy pumps must be working one thousand times faster than they do inside our Sun.

If, on the other hand, we compare our Sun with a dwarf of intrinsic brightness one one-hundred-thousandth, and mass equal to one tenth, we find that the atomic energy pumps inside the very faint dwarf star should be working at a rate of only one ten thousandth of those inside our Sun.

We shall see that these huge differences in the rates of energy generation inside the stars have profound consequences for all theories of stellar evolution. A very faint dwarf star sends out liberated energy at such a slow rate that it can continue to do so for cosmically very long times without a marked depletion of its energy sources, but a supergiant can obviously not continue on its spendthrift ways for cosmically very long times. One conclusion of great evolutionary significance is that the most luminous supergiant stars cannot possibly have existed in their present forms for more than a few million years, a time interval that is ridiculously short in comparison with the probable age of our Earth, which is of the order of 5,000,000,000 years.

The very existence of the supergiant stars forces us immediately to look into the possibility of star birth still being an active process.

The H–R Diagram and the mass luminosity relation summarize in a fair manner prevailing conditions in the section of the Milky Way system in the vicinity of our Sun which, it is well known, is a star on the outskirts of the system, in the region where interstellar dust and gas are relatively plentiful, and where spiral structure is present. About fifteen years ago Walter Baade of Mount Wilson and Palomar Observatories showed conclusively that the familiar H–R Diagram does not even approximately hold for the central part of our Milky Way system, or for the galaxies without spiral structure, the so-called 'ellipsoidal galaxies', which are found interspersed among the spiral galaxies of our Universe.

Baade referred to the varieties of stars exhibited in the traditional H–R Diagram – that is for the region near the Sun – as Population I, and he called the stellar population for the central regions of our own Milky Way system and in the ellipsoidal galaxies, Population II.

The principal characteristic of Population II is that it does not contain at all the luminous supergiants with absolute magnitudes M between -7 and -8, which are so characteristic of our section of the Milky Way system, but, rather, that the brightest giant stars of Population II have values of M between -2 and -3, showing them to be intrinsically one hundredth as bright as the luminous supergiants in the traditional H–R Diagram. To express it differently, in regions of Population II the superluminous stars that must be very young seem to be lacking. Baade envisaged correctly that Population II must represent an older variety of stars, one in which the young and very luminous supergiants have long since burned themselves out. The majority of the subdwarfs and white dwarfs probably belong to this category.

The appearance of a characteristic H–R Diagram for Population II differs markedly from that shown in Fig. 6.1. Some part of the Main Sequence, notably the fainter end, is always present, and a typical Population II Diagram (see Fig. 6.3) shows always a fair number of giant stars with absolute magnitudes running as high as -2 to -3, but the very luminous supergiants are never present.

We have already noted that Population I occurs in regions rich in interstellar gas and dust, the building blocks from which new stars are formed, and we may now add to this that Population II prevails in regions free from interstellar gas and dust. Hence, Population II is found in regions where the formation of new stars is not likely to take place, and we rather expect to find mostly old stars in these parts. For our section of the Milky Way luminous supergiant – hence young – stars are present along with relatively plentiful interstellar gas and cosmic dust; this suggests that we happen to be located in a section of the Milky Way system where star birth is still a relatively common phenomenon. In the Population II sections, star birth has apparently all but ceased.

The age factor is probably the all-important one. In order to understand better the basic phenomena associated with stellar evolution, it would be well to examine the H–R Diagrams for groups of stars 'born' presumably more or less simultaneously. We have such groups in the star clusters of our Milky Way system. There are two varieties of these star clusters, the galactic clusters and the globular clusters.

Galactic clusters are groupings of fifty to about two thousand stars and the diameters of these groupings range roughly between ten and at most one hundred light years. The globular clusters have far greater membership, in some cases running possibly close to one million stars, and their diameters are in the range from fifty to several hundred light years. In addition, we find in our home section of the Milky Way system and in such external objects as the Large Magellanic Cloud, a fair number of very extended loose groupings known as 'associations', most of them noted for the abundance in them of young and very luminous supergiants. Several of these associations possess so many luminous supergiants that one may guess that all of the stars in the association were relatively recently formed.

There are many varieties among the galactic clusters, many of them rich in luminous supergiants, and hence presumably quite recently formed on the cosmic scale, and others without any such supergiants and hence likely to be considerably older. The total absence of luminous supergiants in globular star clusters is indicative of great age for the majority of globular clusters, a conclusion that, we shall see, is strengthened by many independent lines of evidence.

Figs. 6.2 and 6.3 together present the key to an understanding of our present views on stellar evolution. Both figures are in principle H–R Diagrams similar to the one shown in Fig. 6.1. But there is one important difference: we have substituted the so-called colour index for the more familiar spectral type. We mentioned already in our earlier discussion that the horizontal scale, represented by the spectral classes, is in effect a scale of the inverse of the surface temperature of the star, with the high temperatures belonging to the O, B and A stars, and the low temperatures to the K and M stars.

In modern practice, the colour index is a precise and reproducible measure for the colour, and hence the surface temperature, of a star. Such a colour index is measured in the following manner: one measures first the deflection produced as the light from a star is registered on the photoelectric cell after passage through a blue filter, next the same deflection after the star's light passes through a yellow filter. The ratio of these two deflections, transformed to the logarithmic scale of stellar apparent

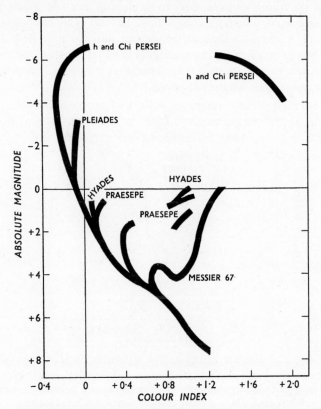

Fig. 6.2. The Hertzsprung–Russell diagram for Seven Galactic Star clusters. A composite diagram prepared by Harold Johnson and Sandage. One notes that the main sequences all converge at the lower end, where there has been insufficient time for appreciable evolution to have taken place, but that they diverge markedly at the upper end where differences in cluster ages produce results that differ markedly from one cluster to the next

magnitudes, yields the quantity known as the colour index. The zero-point is defined by arbitrarily assigning a colour index equal to zero for an average A0 star.

Another way of defining colour index is as the difference in apparent magnitude measured for the star through a blue filter and a yellow filter.

The precise definition of colour index depends, of course, on the filter system employed, but, generally speaking, when the colour index for an A0 star is set to zero, then it becomes equal to $+1\cdot0$ for a K0 to K5 star. A typical blue-white B star has a colour index of $-0\cdot4$, and for a star like our Sun the colour index is likely to be close to the $+0\cdot5$ mark. For a really red giant or dwarf, the colour index may run as high as $+2\cdot0$.

In Figs. 6.2 and 6.3 the scale of spectral class has been replaced by that of colour index. It will be noted that in all three figures the vertical scale remains that of absolute magnitude. Figs. 6.2 and 6.3 are generally referred to as colour-magnitude arrays.

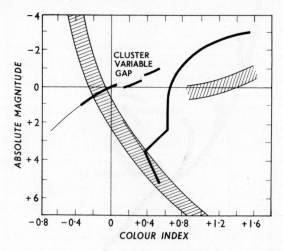

Fig. 6.3. The Colour-Magnitude diagram for the Globular Star Cluster Messier 3. The heavy black line shows the colour-magnitude diagram for the cluster (Population II). The cross-hatched bands show the Hertzsprung–Russell diagram for the region around the Sun (Population I). (From a diagram by Arp, Baum and Sandage.)

In Fig. 6.2, we show the colour-magnitude arrays for a variety of well-studied galactic clusters. The familiar Main Sequence is clearly marked, but the most notable effect is that the more luminous stars seem to fork away from the Main Sequence. This is an observed fact, which is basic to our understanding of the processes of stellar evolution. In Fig. 6.3, we show the colour-magnitude array for a typical globular star cluster, and to remind the reader of the familiar H–R Diagram of Population I, we are showing the Main Sequence and standard Giant Branch by cross hatching in the same diagram. It will be noted that the globular cluster stars with absolute magnitudes M between $+4$ and $+6$ fall pretty well along the standard Main Sequence, but the more luminous stars fall along wholly unfamiliar branches in the colour-magnitude array.

To give a bit of advance perspective on the problems of stellar evolution, we describe briefly the general characteristics of the probable evolutionary paths in the H–R Diagram. A star begins its life as a small cloud of interstellar gas on the verge of gravitational collapse. Once started, the process of gravitational collapse is a relatively rapid one, and in cosmically very short times – often only a few million years – the star contracts from a small cloud of interstellar gas to become a Main Sequence star. The precise place where the star joins the Main Sequence is determined by the mass of the collapsing body of gas. During the process of collapse the star shines with gradually increasing brightness at the expense of the released gravitational potential energy. Once the star arrives at the Main Sequence, contraction ceases and the required energy to keep the star shining is produced from here on by sub-atomic transformation. Initially, the star may be supposed to be rich in hydrogen, which provides a steady source of atomic fuel for the time during which the star remains on the Main Sequence. Stars with masses equal to and lower than that of the Sun derive their energy from the proton–proton reaction, which leads to the building of helium nuclei through the direct interaction between protons, with the consequent mass-loss released in the form of nuclear energy. In stars with masses in excess of three solar masses the carbon cycle is at work. It is a process in which the carbon nuclei act as catalysts to produce the same net result of transforming protons into helium nuclei. In stars with masses between that of the Sun and three times as great, both processes may operate simultaneously, the carbon cycle in the central parts and the proton–proton reaction in the outer shells of the star's interior core.

As the hydrogen in the interior core begins to be exhausted, the star expands with the shell, or shells, of nuclear burning moving gradually outward, away from the star's centre. Stars with masses comparable to that of the Sun will grow in diameter and increase rather rapidly in absolute magnitude. Such a star gradually moves away from the Main Sequence toward the red giants. For a relatively short time it is actually a red giant and at this point hydrogen burning ceases and atomic transformations involving helium nuclei take over as sources of internal stellar energy. In the process, the star will probably lose some of its mass by an ejection process, but the end is in sight and the star is presumably headed shortly for the faint and semi-permanent state of a white dwarf.

We noted already that the contraction stage of evolution is a relatively brief one. A star like our Sun stays on the Main Sequence for several thousand million years, the more massive stars for shorter periods. Once the star leaves the Main Sequence, its evolution goes on at an accelerated pace – and the helium-burning stages (which follow the red giant stage) are also traversed quickly on the cosmic scale. It is not surprising that the majority of stars is observed either on the Main Sequence or in the white dwarf stage.

Now let us return to Fig. 6.2. The galactic clusters h and Chi Persei, which are rich in supergiants of all sorts, have a well-defined Main Sequence. The blue-white giants and supergiants with negative colour indices are so nicely aligned on the traditional Main Sequence that one estimates that the age of this cluster can hardly be more than one million years since its formation from the interstellar gas.

For the Pleiades cluster, the turn-off point already comes at a fainter absolute magnitude, and here an age since formation of the order of twenty to thirty million years is suggested.

Two other familiar galactic clusters, the Hyades and Praesepe, fork off at absolute magnitudes that suggest ages since formation close to 500 million years, whereas the galactic cluster known by the name of Messier 67 may have been in existence more than ten times as long, approximately 6000 million years, which is already in excess of the probable age of the Sun and Earth.

The connection with the globular cluster diagram in Fig. 6.3 is now clear; in the globular star cluster Messier 3, we have a case for which all stars brighter than absolute magnitude $M = +4$ have already evolved away from the Main Sequence, and Fig. 6.3 suggests a probable age for Messier 3 equal to twice that for the old galactic cluster Messier 67.

Our studies of colours and magnitudes in galactic and globular clusters have revealed probable evolutionary ages for groups of stars as a whole, ranging from the cosmically very short time of about one million years for the Perseus Cluster to a value close to 10,000,000,000 years for a typical globular cluster; possibly twice as long for the oldest.

Some galactic clusters may be dated in two ways. They are young clusters that have in them stars of a wide range of absolute magnitude. Here the bright supergiants have already evolved sufficiently to have turned away from the Main Sequence, whereas some of the fainter stars are still in the contraction stage and have not yet reached the Main Sequence. One value of the cluster's age can be found from the location of the turning-off point at bright absolute magnitude, another from the position on the Main Sequence that marks the place at which appear the first stars that are caught still in the process of gravitational contraction.

A recent example of a cluster of this sort was studied by Arthur R. Hogg at Mount Stromlo Observatory. He found for a cluster centred on the star Velorum, a nuclear age from the upper turning-off point in the range twenty-five to fifty million years, and, from the place where the faint stars deviate definitely from the standard Main Sequence, a contraction age of thirty-five million years – fair agreement on the cosmic scale.

One final comment remains to be made: initial chemical composition, along with the initial mass and the age of a star, determine its state. We have already considered the effects of mass and age, which are basically that the more massive stars evolve infinitely faster than the less massive ones. What about chemical composition?

Here some fine distinctions arise. From the astrophysicist's point of view, there are only three major components to the interior of a star, hydrogen, helium, and all the other elements grouped together under the name of metals. Under this terminology, carbon, nitrogen and oxygen are called metals. As the hydrogen and helium supplies become gradually exhausted during the evolutionary processes, the metal abundance increases. The percentage of 'metals' present in the star's interior has important effects on the evolutionary paths followed by the stars. Recent calculations by F. Hoyle and others have shown that in the early evolutionary stages stars with a wide range of metal abundances all lie very close to a single Main Sequence. Differences appear once the stars leave the Main Sequence. The precise evolutionary tracks for stars with masses of the order of magnitude of that of our Sun differ considerably depending on the metal abundance. Stars of low metal abundance – those of the globular clusters for example – will become red giants with absolute magnitudes close to $- 2\cdot5$, whereas a star like our Sun, with a considerable admixture of metals, will probably never become as bright as $M =$ zero in its red giant stage. The chances are that, following the red giant stage, most stars will head towards oblivion as white dwarfs.

If ejection of matter from the star's surface plays as major a part as seems indicated, then the ejected gases may be quite rich in metals and thus increase gradually the metal abundance of the interstellar gas. The stars that are being formed now from the interstellar gas may well be considerably richer in metals than those formed at earlier stages in the development of our Universe. Variations in metal abundance and different rates of ejection of mass at various evolutionary stages will appreciably affect the evolutionary paths in the H–R Diagram that are followed by stars which, at first sight, may seem much alike.

The distinction between metal-poor and metal-rich stars can be made observationally in a variety of ways. The most obvious and direct approach is through measurement of abundances of various chemical elements directly from the strength of the spectral lines observed in high dispersion spectrographs. The stellar spectroscopist obviously has important contributions to make in this field. A new approach of great promise has been developed by Strömgren, who measures the colour characteristics of stars with the aid of narrow-band filters. The great advantage of Strömgren's technique is that it can be applied to very faint and distant stars, objects that could not readily be reached by standard spectroscopic techniques. Comparative studies of the colour properties of metal-rich and metal-poor stars, covering a wide range of wavelengths with standard colour filters for sections of the spectrum from the ultraviolet to the infrared, also promise great benefits for the future.

Currently, much attention is being given to the processes of the gradual building up of the basic chemical elements in stellar interiors. Laboratory evidence and theory concur in showing that the basic structures of the atomic nuclei remain intact in the gas clouds of interstellar space, at least under the density and temperature conditions prevailing there at present. Most atom building must take place inside the stars, at minimum temperatures of several million degrees; the only occasion on which any of it takes place outside the star is possibly in the nebula resulting from a supernova explosion.

We have already noted that the simplest process for the building of helium nuclei from hydrogen nuclei – protons – is the simple proton–proton interaction by which a stable helium nucleus is formed in three steps. This is the principal reaction at work inside the stars of the Main Sequence, similar to or less massive than the Sun, with internal temperatures of the order of fifteen million degrees or so. In the interiors of the Main Sequence stars with masses considerably greater than that of the Sun, the carbon cycle achieves the same purpose—building helium nuclei from protons, with attendant loss of mass, hence liberation of atomic energy—with the carbin nuclei needed to trigger the reaction. The carbon cycle is highly temperature-dependent—as the sixteenth to twentieth power of the temperature—whereas the proton–proton chain is less so—as the fourth power of the temperature.

As the star uses its supply of available hydrogen atomic fuel, the internal temperature will rise until helium reactions begin to take effect at temperatures in the one hundred million degrees range. Apart from some rather transitory light elements, the chemical elements produced in this process are principally carbon, oxygen, neon and magnesium, all with atomic weights divisible by four, which is indicative of stability; the atomic weights are respectively 12, 16, 20 and 24. These are the processes primarily at work in the red giants. When the temperature exceeds one hundred million degrees, three helium nuclei can combine to form one carbon nucleus. The simultaneous collision of three bodies is demanded; hence no direct laboratory check is possible, although the inverse reaction (disintegration of an isomer of carbon into three helium particles) has been verified at the California Institute of Technology. Once carbon is formed, subsequent helium particle capture is relatively easy, so neon, magnesium, silicon and sulphur can be formed.

The internal helium supply then becomes exhausted, but gravitational contraction continues in the interior with resultant increases in temperature, which rises in the central parts to one thousand million degrees. Atomic nuclei with weights divisible by four are still being formed, and as the temperature rises, even calcium, with an atomic weight of 40, is produced. At temperatures greater than three thousand million degrees more interactions follow and we must assume that these are needed to produce elements such as iron, titanium, chromium, manganese and nickel. One should bear in mind that at these high temperatures nuclear reactions go on almost as freely as chemical reactions in an oil-refinery process, and the iron peak of abundance is truly an equilibrium phenomenon. Free neutrons play an important role in the building of the elements with atomic weights not divisible by four, and they assist also in the building of the elements heavier than iron – atomic weights in excess of 56. The needed neutrons are probably produced as a by-product of interactions involving protons and helium nuclei, brought about by internal mixing from the outer zones into the hydrogen and helium-exhausted cores.

How can the astrophysicist check on the probable correctness of these processes which are presumably at work in the star's interiors? Laboratory evidence and extensive calculations are of great assistance, but certain observational checks are needed. The most powerful check comes from the observed distribution curve of abundance of the chemical elements. The compilation of abundances of elements in the solar system (or the average for our part of the galaxy) is a difficult task that involves the use of solar and stellar data to fix the general run of the abundance curve, but the details are filled in by using information gathered from gaseous nebulae, the Earth's crust and especially chondritic meteorites. Such empirical abundance compilations have been attempted by Harrison Brown, by Suess and Urey, and most recently by Aller, who was strongly influenced by the results obtained in the Michigan star abundance work (Goldberg, Muller and Aller). The results are shown in

Fig. 6.4, where the different elements and their probable mechanisms of origin are displayed.

The relative abundances (by numbers of atoms) are plotted against atomic number (charge on nucleus). The scale is normalized to hydrogen (one million million atoms). Lithium, beryllium and boron are destroyed in stellar interiors and can be produced only by reactions in stellar atmospheres or possibly in objects such as the Crab Nebula. Elements

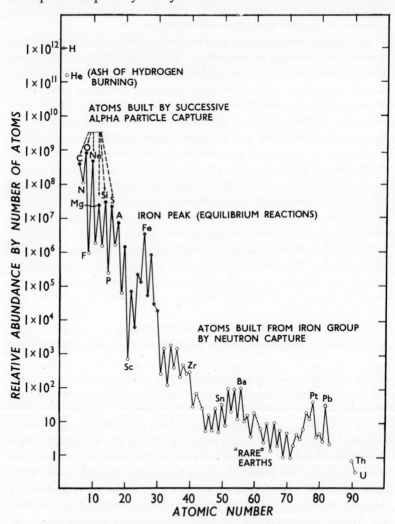

Fig. 6.4. Relative abundances of elements (after L. H. Allen)

such as carbon, oxygen, neon, magnesium, silicon and sulphur are built by successive helium nucleus (alpha particle) captures. Elements near iron, e.g. manganese, copper, cobalt and nickel are formed at high temperatures and densities where nuclei are broken down by impact with one another and the most stable nuclei are favoured. Heavier elements which are really relatively rare are mostly formed by adding neutrons to elements in the iron group. Lead is formed largely by cyclical nuclear reactions following element build-up in fast nuclear reactions in a supernova explosion.

In the Sun, 90 per cent of all atoms are hydrogen atoms, which account for more than 70 per cent of the total mass of matter inside stars and in interstellar space. Helium atoms are less than 10 per cent of the total in number, about 25 per cent in weight. All other atoms together account for 1 to 2 per cent of the total mass. Among the heavier elements, those with atomic weights divisible by four are actually favoured. The percentage abundances of all elements with atomic weights and numbers greater than those of iron are extremely low. The abundances of most of the heavier elements are less than one hundred-thousandth of that for iron.

One of the most direct checks on the effectiveness of the atomic transformations now at work comes from the identification by Merrill of the unstable element technetium in the spectra of the cool stars of spectral type S. Technetium has a half life, before further transformation, of only about 200,000 years, and it must have been produced in element-building processes at temperatures in excess of one thousand million degrees. Hence, such high temperatures must have prevailed in our Universe within cosmically recent times. Supernova explosions may provide the necessary conditions. They are probably caused in part by the temporary going out of control of the processes of atom building, and much of the enrichment of the interstellar gas in heavy elements may result from these explosions.

All told, the recent theoretical and laboratory studies of atomic transformations – Gamow, Salpeter, Cameron, Fowler, the Burbidges and Hoyle – coupled with the observational studies of Aller, Greenstein, Schwarzschild and many others, have given us a convincing and comprehensive first picture of the probable general outline of atom building in space.

The presence of metals and other heavy elements in interstellar space, and in the Sun and other stars, suggests that a steady cycle is in progress of star formation from the interstellar gas, followed by gas returned to interstellar space by ejection from stars or by stellar explosions. At the start atom building progressed apparently at a very fast rate, but while it has probably slowed down considerably, it has by no means stopped. The first generation of stars was presumably very rich in hydrogen, but those that were formed several thousand million years after the formation of the Universe were formed from interstellar gas already enriched with heavier elements. Our Sun is at least a second-generation star and possibly of third generation.

CHAPTER 7

Interstellar Gas and Cosmic Dust

The evidence presented in the first chapter shows conclusively that stars with masses equal to ten to one hundred times that of the Sun should evolve quite rapidly. The maximum ages that we assign to some of the apparently very young stars are of the order of one to ten million years.

One should bear in mind that on the cosmic scale ten million years is just an instant. It represents one twentieth of the time that it takes our Sun and most of the stars near us to circle once around the centre of our Milky Way system, and it is no more than one five-hundredth part of the probable age of our solar system.

We are thus forced to consider the possibility that these cosmically very young stars are still being formed today from the matter that is present in interstellar space, that is from the interstellar gas and cosmic dust. We observe in many nearby parts of our Milky Way system regions that have an abundance of interstellar gas and cosmic dust and which are also relatively rich in young and super-luminous O and B stars. These extensive complexes of gaseous nebulosity appear to possess all the attributes required for places where star formation is now taking place.

The region of the Orion Nebula and its associated O and B stars is a case in point. The Southern Hemisphere astronomer is fortunate in having some of the prize samples within his domain: the Great Nebula around Eta Carinae and the 30 Doradus Nebula are good examples. We must obviously look carefully into the properties of interstellar matter if we wish to come to an understanding of the conditions that will favour the formation of new stars.

The most conspicuous manifestation of the presence of the inter-stellar gas is through the bright and beautiful emission nebulae, large and tenuous clouds of luminous gas. The three nebulae to which we have just referred are in this class. What do we know about their composition, average density and fluctuations in density of the gas within them, and by what processes are they made to shine?

According to the best available estimates, hydrogen atoms account for approximately 65 per cent of the total gas density in an emission nebula, with helium taking care of most of the remainder. Oxygen and calcium are probably next on the list, but their abundance amounts to less than one tenth of one per cent compared with hydrogen and helium, and the abundances of the elements to follow, sodium, potassium and titanium, are smaller again by an order of magnitude.

Hydrogen is obviously the key element of interstellar space. It is fortunate that the hydrogen atom represents also the atom most desired for purposes of star formation and evolution. The average densities within the large emission nebulae are of the order of 50 to 100 hydrogen atoms cm^3, which is far less than in the most perfect vacuum that we may obtain in the physical laboratory. The extents of the emission nebulae are very great, with diameters often of the order of one hundred light years. The total masses of the nebulae or complexes of nebulosity may be as high as 25,000 to 50,000 solar masses, and we are thus assured that there exists within the boundaries of a large emission nebula plenty of gaseous matter for possible condensation into new stars.

The emission nebulae are not self-luminous. They derive their luminescence from the presence within their boundaries of hot, blue-white O and B stars, which stars – with surface temperatures of the order of 20,000° K and higher – emit plentiful ultraviolet radiation. This ultraviolet radiation ionizes the available neutral hydrogen atoms, thus producing an abundant supply of protons and free electrons within the nebula.

Not infrequently, the free and negatively-charged electrons recombine with the positively charged protons, and such captures are often made in the higher energy levels of the neutral hydrogen atom. The hydrogen atom will, of course, stay in the excited state for only a very short time, and, as the electron cascades down to the lowest or Lyman level, lines from the familiar neutral hydrogen series, Balmer, Paschen and Lyman, are produced in emission, thus making the nebula accessible to observation from the Earth.

We possess at present many different techniques for the study of the emission nebulae. Best known of these is the straightforward optical analysis based on spectral observations of the Balmer lines of neutral atomic hydrogen. Additional information is obtained from researches on spectral lines produced by other elements in various stages of ionization, notably helium, oxygen, nitrogen and carbon. To supplement spectral studies of emission nebulae, we require measurements of total brightnesses and of the distribution of surface brightness over the face of each extended nebula. The photometry of emission nebulae is often done with the aid of interference filters, which isolate the radiations emitted by a single spectral line, or a small group of neighbouring lines.

Radio techniques contribute much useful information. As a by-product of the recombination process between electrons and protons, a gaseous nebula emits strong and by now easily detectable radio radiation, especially in the range of radio wavelengths from 1 to 20 cm. With some difficulty, we may detect this sort of radiation even from studies at greater wavelengths, all the way to the metre range. At the longest radio wavelengths, that are received from outer space, the emission nebulae are seen as dark spots against an illuminated sky, since at these wavelengths the emission nebulae act as effective absorbers of radiation that reaches our Earth from the more remote parts of our Milky Way system and from the universe of galaxies.

The study of emission nebulae in the far ultraviolet holds great promise for the future, but, because of absorption of ultraviolet radiation in our Earth's atmosphere, such studies will perforce have to be done from high-flying balloons, rockets or Earth satellites. At the moment, the rocket approach seems most likely to yield immediate results. Already very interesting information has been obtained from rocket flights in the United States, and in Australia, to heights of the order of one hundred miles with apparatus capable of recording radiations in the wavelength range 1200 to 1400 Angstroms.

At the wavelength of Lyman Alpha (1215 Å) the whole of the night sky appears to be bright, but at wavelengths between 1225 Å and 1350 Å the familiar emission nebulae begin to show and some unexpected new regions of emission are detected. Space research promises important contributions to our knowledge of the physical properties of emission nebulae, and, as in so many other fields of astronomical research, the Southern Hemisphere possesses the regions of greatest interest and at Woomera a very fine rocket range.

Since we are here primarily concerned with the evolutionary status of the interstellar gas, we should stress immediately the highly irregular distribution of this gas as we observe it. Many nebulae exhibit a beautiful but far from smooth structure which, in itself, already suggests an approach to the formation of condensations.

Recent physical studies of detailed properties of emission nebulae have added to this general picture. It appears that perhaps the best physical model for a large emission nebula is one in which the mass is concentrated mostly in fairly dense small clouds, with all the clouds together occupying only 3 or 4 per cent of the total volume of the nebula.

This model was arrived at wholly from the theoretical interpretation of observed data on spectral distribution and surface brightness of certain large emission nebulae. If it is substantiated by further observation and analysis, then it provides us at once with a model suggestive of incipient star formation.

Emission nebulae represent concentrations in the interstellar gas, but they are by no means the whole story. We have evidence that in the part of our Milky Way system where our Sun is located, there is much inter-stellar gas outside the nebulae proper, concentrated largely within a layer of a thousand light years thickness near the central plane of our Milky Way system. The average gas density is only about 1 per cent of that in the large nebular complexes, of the order of one hydrogen atom per cubic centimetre.

The gas is concentrated in a ten-to-one ratio to the spiral arms of our Milky Way system, but it is apparently found in varying amounts every-where close to the central plane, at least in the outer parts. We have several ways of detecting this more thinly distributed interstellar gaseous medium. Some of the filter techniques to which we referred above assist us in obtaining information regarding the properties of the interstellar gas close to the central plane of our Milky Way system. In addition, the radio astronomical techniques, employing the 21-cm line of neutral hydrogen, and the optical technique of observing interstellar absorption lines, help to round out the picture.

The 21 cm line is produced by the neutral hydrogen atom. It will be remembered that the Lyman level represents the lowest energy level of the neutral hydrogen atom. It possesses no regular 'fine structure', but it does have 'hyper-fine structure', which is determined by differences in orientation of the magnetic spin of the outer electron and the corres-ponding magnetic spin of the atomic nucleus.

One level corresponds to the case of parallel spins of nucleus and electron, the other to oppositely directed spins. The difference in energy between the two hyper-fine levels corresponds to a quantum with a wavelength of 21 cm. A single hydrogen atom will probably emit such a quantum only once every 300 years or so, but the number of neutral hydrogen atoms along a line of sight is so great that we do receive on Earth sufficient radiation at 21 cm wavelength to detect it with our large radio telescopes.

The search for 21 cm radiation with a highly directional radio-teles-cope yields first of all the directions from which we receive the greatest amounts of 21 cm radiation and, from the total intensities that are recorded, we can deduce roughly how much hydrogen there is along the particular line of sight.

If all the hydrogen in our galaxy were at rest relative to the Sun and Earth, then we would receive only one very narrow line in the radio spectrum. But our Milky Way system is by no means at rest and the clouds of hydrogen at various distances from the galactic centre move with different speeds around the centre. In addition, the hydrogen clouds have motions of their own, and all these motions combined give us a Doppler pattern of considerable complexity.

From the appearance of the intensity profile (intensity versus precise wavelength) of the 21 cm line observed for any particular direction, we may deduce how much neutral atomic hydrogen there is present for that direction at given radial velocities of approach and recession. If we possess – as we do – a rotational model for motions in our Milky Way system, then we can assign to each observed radial velocity of approach or recession a given distance from the Earth, and thus we find how much hydrogen there is present at various distances from the Sun for each given direction.

From analysis of this sort one may obtain a complete picture of the distribution of neutral atomic hydrogen in our Milky Way system. The 21 cm line has become a most useful item in our astronomical tool chest, for through it we now have access for the first time to the most common form of hydrogen in interstellar space: neutral atomic hydrogen.

The reader will remember from our earlier description that the optical Balmer lines in the spectra of emission nebulae were produced as a by-product of the capture of free electrons by protons and it is thus clear that the optical observations of the Balmer lines will tell us only about the amounts of protons and free electrons present in space and that these observations would by themselves give no clues as to the presence of neutral atomic hydrogen.

The 21 cm observations assist us in rounding out our picture of the interstellar gas in a variety of ways. First of all, they serve to delineate more clearly than any other type of observation the spiral structure of our Milky Way system. Second, they supplement our information on the density in space of neutral atomic hydrogen. Thirdly, these observations provide us with an increasingly detailed picture of the cloud structure of the interstellar medium and, together with this information, we obtain useful data regarding average densities, temperatures, masses and motions of these neutral atomic hydrogen clouds.

The angular resolution of existing radio telescopes is not yet sufficient to give us the full picture of hydrogen cloud dimensions, but with several large precision radio telescopes now in operation and improved techniques for recording faint radiations already well under development, it should not be many years before the fine structure of the clouds in the interstellar gas will be fully revealed by radio methods.

Radio observations of the continuum and of the 21 cm line permit us to estimate rather closely the total amount of interstellar gas that is present in our Milky Way system. We estimate the total mass of our galaxy, stars, gas and dust combined, at about one hundred thousand million solar masses, but present results suggest that only 2 per cent of this total is accounted for by the interstellar gas, mostly neutral atomic hydrogen, with ionized hydrogen contributing only 5 per cent of the total average gas density.

For simple dynamical reasons, it appears that the density of the hydrogen gas in the part of interstellar space near the Sun represents a higher fraction of the total density than the average for our galaxy. In our parts of the Milky Way system, where, it is remembered, spiral structure prevails, the total density of the interstellar hydrogen gas may well account for 10 to 15 per cent of the density of gas and stars combined.

We now turn briefly to one other important manner in which we may obtain information about the interstellar gas through the application of optical-spectroscopic techniques. High-dispersion spectra of distant stars generally show a certain number of sharp and well-defined absorption lines, which are produced by clouds of interstellar gas located between the star under observation and the Sun and Earth.

These sharp absorption lines are produced especially by neutral and ionized calcium, neutral sodium, potassium and iron, and by ionized titanium. Quite often one observes several components of a given interstellar absorption line, each of which is sharp and well defined. Each component is apparently produced by a cloud along the line of sight, with its own special radial velocity of approach or recession. In one case as many as seven components have been observed for a single absorption line, suggesting the presence of seven distinct interstellar clouds between the Sun and Earth, and the star in the spectrum of which the complex set of lines was found.

Through the study of interstellar absorption lines in the optical range, we can obviously learn much about the cloud structure of the interstellar gaseous medium. Great promise lies in future combined researches of optical-spectroscopic studies for regions that show stars with multiple interstellar absorption lines, coupled with high-resolution 21 cm studies of these same sections of the heavens.

Cosmic dust plays a spectacular but relatively minor role when compared with the interstellar gas. Whenever one photographs a Milky Way field, proof of the presence of cosmic dust is there for all to see. It is often shown in the form of dark lanes observed against a rich, starry back-

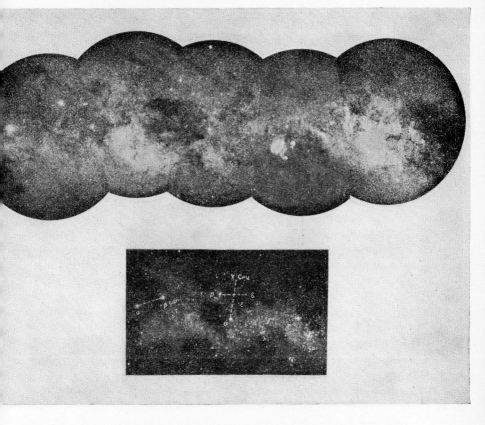

Fig. 7.1. A composite photograph of a section of the Southern Milky Way. The composite at the top is based on five separate photographs in red ($H\alpha$) light of the section of the Milky Way, from the Eta Carinae Nebula (on the right) past the Southern Cross and the Coalsack (left of centre) to Beta and Alpha Centauri (on the left). (Photographs by A. W. Rodgers with the Mount Stromlo 8-inch, $f/1$, Schmidt Telescope.)

The lower photograph by A. R. Hogg serves as a key. It is taken with a small camera and the choice of emulsion suppresses the red ($H\alpha$) light of the nebular emissions. The nebulae are mostly absent in the key, but the familiar visual star patterns come out clearly. The stars Alpha and Beta Centauri, the Southern Cross, Lambda Centauri and the region of Eta Carinae are all marked in white on the key photograph. The Southern Coalsack is slightly below and to the left of the Southern Cross. The distance from Alpha Centauri to Eta Carinae in the sky is approximately 30°

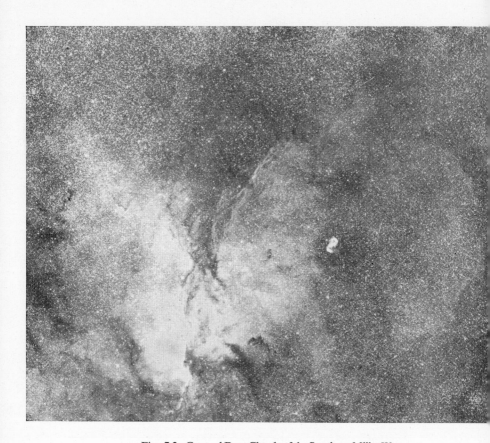

Fig. 7.2. Gas and Dust Clouds of the Southern Milky Way.

Viewed against the mass of emission nebulosity in the lower left of the photograph can be seen several dark streaks and patches produced by overlying clouds and wisps of cosmic dust. The S-shaped nebula to the right of and below the centre of the photograph represents the atmosphere shed by a star located at its centre, which star is apparently in rotation. (From a photograph made by Dr. Bengt E. Westerlund with the 20–26-inch Schmidt Telescope of the Uppsala Station at Mount Stromlo Observatory) ground, and it is seen in its most spectacular form projected against the large emission nebulae.

Some of the clouds of cosmic dust – we call them dark nebulae – can readily be seen with the naked eye. Everyone who has looked at the beautiful southern Milky Way knows how to recognize the Southern Coalsack, located directly east of the Southern Cross. The dark regions and channels of obscuring matter which overlie the brilliant central section of our Milky Way system in Sagittarius and Scorpius are all effects produced by dense complexes of cosmic dust.

Through studies of the discoloration and polarization produced by cosmic dust in the light of a star that lies beyond one of the dust clouds, we can deduce much useful information about the particles which populate the clouds of cosmic dust. The most common type of particle seems to be a slightly elongated one with an average diameter of the order of one one-hundred-thousandth of an inch. It is composed in all likelihood of molecular combinations of familiar elements, such as carbon, nitrogen, oxygen and the ever-present hydrogen.

The cosmic dust particles seem to have strong tendencies to occur in clouds of various sizes. The Southern Coalsack is but one example of such a cloud. We estimate it to have a diameter of about ten light years and a total dust mass of between 30 and 50 solar masses. There exist a few larger complexes of dust clouds, but the Southern Coalsack represents one of the larger and more massive structures.

There are many very much smaller dark nebulae, some of them highly concentrated features generally referred to as 'globules'. These have diameters sometimes as small as one hundredth of a light year, which is comparable to the dimensions of an outsized solar system.

While it is impossible to give more than a lower limit for the probable masses of the globules, it seems as though these limits should be of the order of the mass of our Sun, certainly not much greater. The larger complexes of cosmic dust have neutral atomic hydrogen associated with them – this has been demonstrated through 21 cm observations – and in the few established cases it appears that the neutral atomic hydrogen has a probable total mass equal to one hundred times that of the cosmic dust. No such data are yet available for the smaller dust features, such as the larger globules.

Present-day astrophysics regards the cosmic dust as a spectacular, but rather minor, component of the interstellar medium. The best estimates available today suggest that the cosmic dust by itself accounts for only 1 or at most 2 per cent of the total mass of the interstellar medium. The student of stellar evolution has, however, a great interest in the cosmic dust.

First of all, the tiny dust particles are probably dragged along by the surrounding gas, and the dust features serve rather effectively as tracers for the gas.

Second, we observe a great many very fine dust features, notably the globules, and these still seem to be the most likely candidates for nuclei around which we might hope to build newly formed stars. The presence of abundant cosmic dust, along with emission nebulosity, in many associations and clusters of O and B stars should be noted at this point.

Occasionally fairly dense clouds of cosmic dust occur in the vicinity of relatively bright and cool stars, or of a group of stars, and then the dark nebula is found to shine by reflected light: a reflection nebula. The Pleiades cluster has a fine and very delicate reflection nebula associated with it. From the study of the properties of this reflected light, we can learn much about particle dimensions and about the electrical properties of these tiny particles, thus confirming our conclusions about shapes, particle sizes and composition already mentioned above.

Several emission nebulae exhibit small globules in considerable numbers at their outer edges. The student of stellar evolution will obviously ask how these tiny globules are held together, and if they are being further compressed.

It seems not unlikely that these tiny dark clouds are a mixture of gas and dust now in the process of contraction. They will, first of all, tend to contract under their own gravitational action, and a collapse, once started, will be a self-accelerating process. They will be aided in their collapse by the radiation pressure exerted from the outside upon the globule, and probably even more by the high gas pressure exerted by the ionized gas at the boundary region between ionized neutral hydrogen. Finally, magnetic forces may play their part in further squeezing the globule together.

We do not suppose that all globules will collapse in a neat and predictable fashion. More likely many of the observed objects are of a highly temporary nature, to be blown to bits by what we might loosely call the cosmic winds. But an occasional globule should encounter conditions which would encourage collapse, and collapse once started will eventually almost certainly lead to a thin and very extended star, set on the first steps of its evolutionary path as discussed in the preceding chapter.

There is another way in which incipient star formation seems to be connected with interstellar gas and dust. In the vicinity of some of the best-known dark nebulae very faint variable stars have been discovered, which appear to be dwarf-like stars rather recently formed. These 'T

Tauri variables' are now generally recognized as the first observed stages of a star in evolution. In two cases it has even been suspected that we may have seen a T-Tauri variable become bright before our eyes within a very few years. Obviously this concept of the formation of new stars from interstellar gas and dust appears to be a fruitful one.

While we are confident of the correctness of our present general approach to problems of stellar evolution, there remain many puzzles to be solved. Normally one would expect the interstellar gas to be distributed fairly evenly over the thin central layer, but, for reasons not yet understood, the interstellar gases in our Milky Way system and other spiral galaxies seem to follow a neat spiral pattern. Associated with these spiral arms we find large-scale magnetic fields, so aligned that the lines of force follow the spiral pattern reasonably closely. Presumably these magnetic lines of force serve to concentrate the interstellar gas principally in the spiral arms, and these same magnetic forces may well affect the evolution of small gas clouds in the spiral arms.

The tracing of the spiral arms of our own galaxy has been a far from simple process. The tentative diagram favoured by the astronomers of Mount Stromlo Observatory is shown in Fig. 7.3. The radio features are sketched in according to the 21 cm results of the analysis by F. J. Kerr and associates, of the Radiophysics Laboratory in Sydney, and the optical features have been assembled by the Stromlo group from various sources. Most recent work lends support to the suggestion that, at least for the vicinity of the Sun, the spiral features have nearly circular shapes centred upon the centre of our galaxy.

The most unexpected new results in recent years have been for the region near the galactic centre. Radio studies in Holland have shown that much ionized and neutral atomic hydrogen is, surprisingly, present in the central part of our galaxy, and there is every indication that the hydrogen clouds near the galactic centre, already assembled in a disc relatively thin perpendicular to the galactic plane, are expanding outward in the plane at a fast rate, ranging between 50 and 200 km per second. The observations give strong evidence for an expanding hydrogen mass at a distance of not more than ten thousand light years from the centre of our Milky Way system. Some of the radio evidence gathered by Kerr suggests that even near the Sun the gas in the spiral arms is still going outward at a rate of 7 km per second.

We are at present very much in the dark with regard to the origin of the interstellar gas in the nucleus of our galaxy. One suggestion that has been made – neither very likely nor very attractive – is that this hydrogen gas comes from flares or minor explosions that are observed in the varieties of dwarf stars which in all likelihood populate the central regions of our galaxy. Another, and to my mind more attractive suggestion, is that the gas is by some mechanism sucked from the outer galacitc halo into the nuclear parts of our galaxy; the flow of this gas is possibly controlled by weak, large-scale magnetic fields. This thin galactic halo is also considered the most likely place of origin for high-energy cosmic rays, accelerated there by weak but very extensive varying magnetic fields. Studies made by Drake and others at the National Radio Astronomy Observatory at Green Bank, West Virginia, suggest a very complex situation in the most central parts of our galaxy. Observations

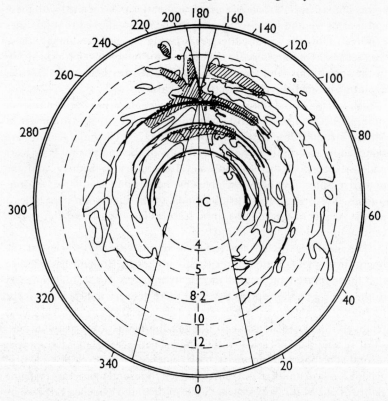

Fig. 7.3. The spiral structure of the Galaxy (Stromlo Model). A comparison of models of spiral structure (1961). The contours are drawn from F. J. Kerr's representation of the Radio Galaxy – assuming general expansion for the gas of 7 km per second. The shaded regions and dark circular lines represent interpretations of optical data. The position of the Sun is marked S, that of the centre of the Galaxy C. The distance scale is in kiloparsecs (one kiloparsec equals 3258 light years). New galactic longitudes are shown on the outer rim. (Diagram prepared by J. B. Whiteoak)

near wavelengths of 4 and 22 cm prove conclusively that ionized hydrogen exists there as well as neutral atomic hydrogen.

As a guide to our understanding of the properties of the nucleus of our own Milky Way system, we turn naturally to the Great Spiral Galaxy in Andromeda and ask what are the properties of its nucleus. A very surprising situation exists there, and the nuclei of our own galaxy and of the Andromeda Galaxy are probably quite unlike each other. The Andromeda Spiral has a nucleus of small dimensions, i.e. a radius of about twenty light years, with an absolute magnitude $M = -11\cdot0$, equivalent to three and a half million suns. It possesses an absorption spectrum and – according to a recent Lick Observatory study by Lallemand, Duchesne and Walker – it completes one revolution in about 500,000 years, which means that its period of rotation is between one tenth and one hundredth of that of the surrounding central portions of the inner parts of the Andromeda Spiral Galaxy. The Lick Observatory astronomers consider this nucleus to be a separate dynamical entity, with the diameter of a globular star cluster, but with about one hundred times the mass of an average globular cluster. It has properties very different from those of the suspected gaseous nucleus of our own Milky Way system.

The view is generally accepted today that spiral arms are probably rather transient phenomena. A spiral arm may remain intact for a few galactic revolutions, but the reader will be well aware of the fact that even ten cosmic years represents only a small fraction of the minimum age of our Universe. According to the best available evidence to date, the spiral arms may originate as almost circular 'smoke rings' that are shot out from the central parts of our galaxy. The rate of expansion probably drops gradually as the circular arm moves outwards and, kept intact and aided by the galactic magnetic field, the smoke ring gradually develops into a gaseous spiral arm. Under the influence of gravitational and magnetic forces, much of the gas in the spiral arm shows a tendency to condense into stars, but these young stars, which are no longer subject to magnetic restrictions of motion, move gradually away from the original gas pattern into orbits of their own. The remainder of the gas loses its identity as a component part of the original spiral arm as the arm is gradually wound up.

There is much that remains obscure in the picture of evolving spiral arms we have just sketched. For example, why should it be that new and massive stars in our own and other galaxies are apparently produced from the gas of the spiral arms only in the outer parts? The researches of the years to come should give the answers to these and related questions.

CHAPTER 8

The Universe of Galaxies

We can learn surprisingly much about stellar evolution in our own Milky Way system through careful examination of the properties of the universe of galaxies.

The power of this approach is demonstrated nicely by the discovery of the two stellar Populations. Baade used the 100 in. Hooker reflector at Mount Wilson Observatory – then the largest reflector in the world – to photograph the central and outer regions of the Great Spiral in Andromeda. At the time when he resolved the nucleus of the Andromeda Galaxy into stars, he noted that the brightest stars in the nucleus were intrinsically fully five magnitudes fainter than the brightest stars in the outer parts which show the spiral structure.

Thus came the first clear suggestion of the importance in our Universe of Populations I and II, a concept that has become a basic one for all evolutionary work on our own galaxy.

It is a fortunate circumstance that our Milky Way system is one of a grouping of seventeen galaxies to which we refer generally as the 'Local Group of Galaxies'. The two Star Clouds of Magellan are the most conspicuous nearby members of the Local Group. Because of their rather unordered appearance, they are classified as 'irregular galaxies'. There are three fine 'spiral galaxies' in the Local Group, the Great Spiral in Andromeda, the very fine spiral in Triangulum known as Messier 33, and of course our own Milky Way system.

Then there are ten amorphous 'ellipsoidal galaxies', three of them of the dwarf variety and the remaining seven of more average class. Two of these ellipsoidal galaxies are companions to the Great Spiral in Andromeda.

To complete the census for the Local Group, we list two more irregular galaxies, which are, however, considerably farther away than the Magellanic Clouds. The only variety of spiral galaxy not represented in the Local Group is that of 'Barred Spirals', star systems in which the spiral arms seem to take off from the ends of a large, luminous bar passing through the centre of the galaxy.

The Magellanic Clouds, at present only sketchily explored, are veritable storehouses of evolutionary information. Their distances from us are somewhere between 150 and 200 thousand light years, which, cosmically speaking, places them right in our celestial backyard. It is important to realize that they are less than one tenth the distance from us of the nearest and most spectacular spiral galaxy, the Great Spiral in Andromeda. This means that stars of comparable absolute magnitude in either Magellanic Cloud appear to us more than five magnitudes brighter than would the same stars when observed in the Andromeda Spiral.

The stars in the Magellanic Clouds are obviously far more accessible to observations with our large telescopes than those in the Andromeda Spiral. It happens that the two Magellanic Clouds are extreme Southern Hemisphere objects, their declinations being respectively 69° and 72° South, which makes them wholly inaccessible from Northern Hemisphere observatories.

The Large and Small Magellanic Clouds alone justify the erection of major telescopic equipment in the Southern Hemisphere, such as a 48-inch Schmidt telescope, and also a giant reflector with an aperture of 150 inches or more. With instrumental equipment of that sort, stars of the faint absolute magnitude of our Sun would come within reach, or almost so, whereas existing telescopic equipment in the Southern Hemisphere limits our studies to objects that are three magnitudes brighter in absolute magnitude. In contrast, we might mention that the 200-inch Hale reflector at Mount Palomar does not quite reach stars of absolute magnitude $M = $ zero in the Great Spiral of Andromeda.

The Large Magellanic Cloud offers the greatest opportunities to the student of stellar evolution. It is rich in highly luminous, blue-white O and B stars and stars of high luminosity of other spectral classes. Certain sections of the Large Magellanic Cloud are unusually rich in emission nebulae, which occur principally in the regions of clustering of the O and B stars.

Some of these super-luminous OB associations embedded in emission nebulosity are obviously places where star formation and evolution are active processes. There is much work to be done through careful study, one by one, of the major associations, for from researches of this type one should be able to obtain much information regarding the evolutionary development of newly formed star groupings.

The emphasis has been principally on the determination by photoelectric and photographic techniques of colour-magnitude arrays similar to those shown in Figs. 8.1a and 8.1b for loose groupings (associations) of super-luminous stars in both clouds. Fig. 8.1a shows a colour-magnitude array for an association studied by Dr. B. E. Westerlund; it is for a young grouping with many blue-white supergiant stars. Fig. 8.1b shows a similar array for an older grouping studied by Dr. S. C. B. Gascoigne. The vertical scale is in each case visual absolute magnitude, the horizontal scale the colour index, B-V. Note that the vertical scales are shifted with respect to each other in the two diagrams. The Radcliffe Observatory in South Africa, co-operating with the Royal Greenwich Observatory, and the Mount Stromlo Observatory and the Uppsala Station in Australia have been most active in this field. The striking fact

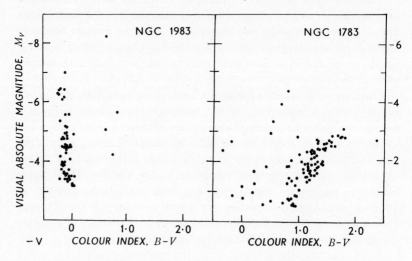

Fig. 8.1a and 8.1b. Two colour magnitude arrays in the Large Magellanic Cloud

that emerges from these researches is that almost all associations embedded in nebulosity have remarkably large numbers of very blue supergiants. Fig. 8.1a gives an example of such a colour-magnitude array. It is suggestive of a very recently formed association, a grouping in which some stars of absolute magnitude $M = -7$ (visual apparent magnitude 12) have not yet even had time to evolve away from the Main Sequence. The presence of much interstellar gas in the region of most of these young groupings, visible as emission nebulosity, supports the hypothesis that here we are looking at places in our Universe in which the evolutionary pots are boiling fiercely. Many of the stars plotted in Fig. 8.1a can hardly have existed for more than a few million years, a ridiculously short time interval on the cosmic scale, something of the order of one hundredth of a cosmic year.

Much interest will, in the years to come, attach to the study of the chemical composition of the gaseous nebulae in the Magellanic Clouds. A first study by Hugh M. Johnson at Mount Stromlo has shown that hydrogen and helium are mixed in approximately the same proportion in the gaseous nebulae of the Milky Way system and in the largest nebula of the Large Magellanic Cloud, 30 Doradus. These results have recently been confirmed and extended by Feast, at Radcliffe Observatory.

A detailed investigation by Aller and Faulkner has been undertaken at Mount Stromlo Observatory. The instrument used is a photoelectric scanner, which combines the advantages of a fast spectrograph with those of a photoelectric cell, recording directly the true total intensities of the emission lines in the nebulae. Aller and Faulkner find as wide a variety of excitation temperatures in the nebulae of the Large and Small Magellanic Clouds as is found in the Milky Way system or the Andromeda Spiral Galaxy. The derived abundance ratios, not only hydrogen to helium but also oxygen to hydrogen and neon to hydrogen, appear to be very nearly the same in the Magellanic Clouds as elsewhere. This most significant result applies equally to the Large Cloud, rich in emission nebulosity, and the Small Cloud, relatively poor in nebulosity. Aller has hazarded the guess that, wherever emission nebulosity and blue stars are found together, the relative abundance of the lighter elements is about the same – a conclusion that should apply to most galaxies of the local group.

It would be a mistake to think of the Magellanic Clouds as composed entirely of new-born stars and star groups. In the Small Cloud the regions of young star groupings and nebulosity are relatively few, and in the Large Cloud they are located mostly in certain sections. The main body of both clouds, as in the main body of the Milky Way system, consists primarily of older stars, and the colour-magnitude arrays for many of the sections without nebulosity in the Magellanic Clouds show much similarity to those found for globular clusters in our Milky Way system, thus suggesting a major component of great antiquity. An example of such a colour-magnitude array is shown in Fig. 8.1b. It is for a decidedly ancient association. In NGC 1783 the most luminous star is four magnitudes fainter intrinsically than the brightest in NGC 1983. Also, the blue giant branch is lacking in NGC 1783, whereas large numbers of red giants are present.

Nowhere in the Universe do we find young and old groupings laid out so neatly side by side as they are in the Large Magellanic Cloud. The unsurpassed richness in star groupings of widely differing evolutionary types, and of stars in all stages of development, makes the Large Cloud the external star system most urgently in need of full study.

We hardly need to stress the importance of future research on the major spiral galaxies in the Local Group. Without the guidance received from earlier studies of the stars and nebulae that populate the spiral arms in these galaxies, we might still be floundering about in our attempts to disentangle the spiral structure of our own Milky Way system.

A few more words need to be said, however, about the evolutionary status of the less spectacular members of the Local Group, the ellipsoidal galaxies. They are devoid of luminous supergiants and their brightest discernible stars are of absolute magnitudes $M = -2$ to -3. They are mostly red giant stars, and the first blue stars do not occur in these objects until about absolute magnitude $M = 0$. Faint traces of gaseous nebulosity are found in a few of them, but in the main one may say that they are lacking in interstellar gas and cosmic dust.

The two dwarf galaxies, star systems in the southern constellations Sculptor and Fornax, are only a little farther away from the Sun than the Magellanic Clouds, but these unspectacular objects were literally missed by many generations of astronomers, and it was almost by accident that Harlow Shapley found them in the mid-thirties. Their colour-magnitude arrays are very much like those for the globular star clusters of our own Milky Way system and they seem in every way like galaxies in which the processes of star formation ceased thousands of millions of years ago, and in which stellar evolution has slowed down to a modest and almost undiscernible pace.

Our rich Southern Hemisphere thus provides the astronomer interested in problems of stellar evolution with the choice extreme samples: the two Magellanic Clouds, in which the evolutionary pots are boiling fiercely, and the near and ancient, unspectacular dwarf galaxies in Sculptor and Fornax.

At this point we should mention one of the most significant basic observations regarding ellipsoidal galaxies, which is that in them we have never found anywhere a spectacular young blue-white supergiant. Walter Baade has made a very thorough search for such supergiants from the beautiful plate material assembled by Edwin Hubble and himself over many years with the 100 and 200 in reflectors in California.

He has stressed repeatedly that the total absence of any such stars, which would be easy to detect, speaks against the hypothesis of the continuous creation of hydrogen, advocated by Hoyle, Bondi, Gold and McCrea.

Baade reasons that in the early stages of stellar evolution, when the ellipsoidal galaxies were still young and full of gas, they must have been magnificent spectacles of smooth galaxies studded with the brilliant, blue-white diamonds of recently born supergiants. He reasons further that in a steady-state universe, as advocated by the group of British cosmologists, one would expect to find ellipsoidal galaxies in earlier stages of evolution as well as the older variety. The existence of only old and worn ellipsoidal galaxies seems to speak against a steady-state universe and generally in favour of one started with a bang and gradually running down; to say it in more dignified form, an evolutionary Universe.

Many astronomers feel a natural revulsion from the hypothesis of continuous creation because of its *ad hoc* character. The cosmologists who advocate this approach now also have to overcome the hurdle of explaining the total absence of youthful supergiant stars in ellipsoidal galaxies.

We naturally ask why it is that evolutionary processes still seem to be quite active in irregular galaxies and in the outer parts of spiral galaxies, while they seem to have come to a halt long ago in ellipsoidal galaxies and in the central regions of spiral galaxies.

It is not so simple to give a straightforward answer to this question, especially when one is asked to deal primarily with the observational aspects of the problem. It seems most likely to be a matter of rotation around a central axis. One notable observational datum about ellipsoidal galaxies is that they are all less flattened than the spiral galaxies.

In the early days of the classification of galaxies, Edwin Hubble noted that the ellipsoidal galaxies never have observed ellipticities greater than 0·7, whereas all of the spiral galaxies were much more flattened. These observations seem to suggest that the principal difference between spiral and ellipsoidal galaxies is a difference in rotational velocities around a central axis, with the spirals rotating relatively much faster than the ellipsoidals.

In the ellipsoidal galaxies, which were turning rather slowly on their axes, the processes of star formation from the initial interstellar gas proceeded rapidly and on a large scale right from the start. The same state of affairs apparently prevailed in the central regions of spiral galaxies, where star formation has by now apparently ceased. In the outer parts of the flattened spiral galaxies, star birth and evolution did not initially progress at a very rapid pace and we still find it at work there today. The observations suggest that rotational speed controls the rate of stellar birth and evolution, but we do not know in precisely what manner these effects operate.

We may count ourselves fortunate that we are located in one of the relatively sparse spots in the Universe, the outer section of a spiral galaxy, where evolutionary processes are still active today. Radio astronomical data, especially that gathered in the Netherlands, show that the total amount of gas available in any given galaxy rarely exceeds 2 per cent of the total mass of that galaxy, and while there might be a slightly greater percentage toward the outer parts, the supply of interstellar gas available for star formation is at present everywhere rather meagre.

Here again the Magellanic Clouds may occupy an extreme position. The observations of the hydrogen content of the Magellanic Clouds made by the radio astronomers in Sydney show that a considerable fraction of the total mass of each cloud is in the form of free interstellar hydrogen. These observations show, furthermore, that both clouds are in rotation, all of which seems to be in accordance with the above suggestions, but all of which requires prompt and careful checking by additional observations.

It might be argued that it is the function of the observing astronomer to observe and report, and not to theorize. I take exception to this point of view, for it is difficult to organize one's observational work properly unless one fits observing programmes to provide critical observational tests of theories and generalized statements. As an observer, I find myself on the side of Walter Baade, who has defended so eloquently the hypothesis that all stellar systems were formed approximately simultaneously, that some have evolved so fast that star birth has ceased in them, but that in others the processes of star birth and evolution are still quite active.

We turn now to more remote parts of the universe of galaxies and enquire what, if any, are the contributions to evolutionary concepts that result from observational studies with powerful telescopic equipment. There are two aspects of special interest. Firstly, we may consider the problems of the large-scale distribution and clustering galaxies, and, secondly, we shall have to touch briefly on the observational basis for the Expanding Universe.

Recent work on the distribution of faint galaxies over the sky and in depth has contributed primarily to our knowledge about the clustering of galaxies in space. For almost thirty years now it has been realized that the phenomenon of clustering is a basically important one for the general distribution of galaxies in space. At first it was thought that there were relatively few major clusters, and that these were superimposed on a smooth general field.

But recent work has more and more tended to show that clustering is a basic property of the universe of galaxies as we know it, and that there may hardly exist any true field galaxies, apart from the relatively few that have escaped from well-defined clusters. During the past few years our knowledge of clusters of galaxies has increased greatly as a result of the close examination of Sky Survey photographs. Numerous well-defined new clusters of galaxies have been discovered and the total number of listed clusters of galaxies now already runs close to two thousand, with each recognized cluster having a minimum membership of approximately fifty galaxies.

There seems to exist a hierarchy of clusters of galaxies, for not infrequently are these clusters found grouped again in bunches of ten or so.

Until a few years ago, most astronomers were of the opinion that all large clusters of galaxies were stable aggregates and hence rather permanent features of the universe of galaxies. Some die-hards – of which the author is one – retain this point of view, but many workers in the field now consider them as rather recently formed groupings, observed to be expanding before our telescopic eyes. The argument in favour of the rapid expansion of most clusters of galaxies runs as follows: the population of galaxies belonging to a given cluster of galaxies may be estimated with fair accuracy and we have apparently enough information to permit us to estimate the total mass of the member galaxies within a factor of about two. While distance estimates leave much to be desired, the consensus of opinion among the experts is that we know them to within ± 50 per cent, and hence the linear dimensions of the cluster of galaxies are known to that accuracy. The other basic data of observation are the velocities measured (as radial velocities) from the Doppler shifts in the spectra of individual member galaxies. The long and short of the argument is that the observed spreads in these velocities are so great that there simply is not enough matter in the galaxies to hold the cluster together gravitationally, and, that hence the whole system must disintegrate in times of the order of a fraction of the age of our solar system, in intervals small compared to the probable age of our Universe. There may be ways out of this dilemma, for most astonomers still dislike the idea of a cluster of galaxies (often containing many apparently very ancient ellipsoidal galaxies) disintegrating in cosmically short times. One possibility (not a likely one) is that our mass estimates of individual galaxies are too small by factors 5 to 10; another, that our radial velocity measurements – technically very difficult – have far larger errors than given by the astronomers who measured them and that, hence, the published velocity spreads are far greater than the real ones. Still another possibility is that there may exist much intergalactic matter associated with clusters of galaxies (molecular hydrogen is a possibility) and that there is after all sufficient mass to hold the system together in spite of the large velocity spread. Anyhow, as of today, we cannot discount the possibility that many of the observed clusters of galaxies may be of recent origin and that we may be forced to abandon the notion that the clusters of galaxies now seen are remnants of groupings formed near the ill-defined 'beginning of things'.

The clustering tendency among galaxies has a very interesting consequence for the total evolutionary picture. Within a cluster, encounters that might be termed 'collisions' are probably not infrequent. What happens if two galaxies actually meet?

As far as the stars are concerned, the consequences will be very minor, and while there might be some gravitational deformation here and there, the two galaxies would probably pass through each other with a minimum of disturbance to the stars. Actual star collisions seem very unlikely.

But the encounter should have grave consequences for any free interstellar gas and cosmic dust within the galaxies. The interstellar matter in the two systems would interact with each other in such a violent manner that toward the end of the collision the gas and dust would be left behind, belonging to neither galaxy, but condemned rather to whirl about in the empty spaces between galaxies.

Walter Baade and Lyman Spitzer were the first to draw attention to the drastic effects that might result from such 'vacuum cleaner' collisions. A spiral galaxy involved in a major collision will probably lose most of the interstellar gas in the spiral arms and with it most of its regenerative power for continued star birth. With its stellar core intact, it might soon become an uninspiring ellipsoidal galaxy. The collision process is probably observed under way in some of the most brilliant radio galaxies.

At the present time, astronomers speak with far less confidence than they did twenty years ago about the distribution in depth of the galaxies. We lack at present the firm foundations for estimating distances of remote galaxies which we thought we possessed twenty years ago.

The reasons for our difficulties are threefold. Firstly, our indicators for distance are far weaker than we thought them to be in the past, and, secondly, we realize now that our measurements of apparent magnitudes are often quite uncertain, and, thirdly, our measured radial velocities may be more in error than we thought possible some years ago.

In recent years our distance estimates for the nearer galaxies, including the members of our Local Group, have undergone major revisions. Our present estimate for the distance of the Great Spiral in Andromeda places it, for example, now at twice the estimated distance generally given ten years ago, and a further upward revision is not altogether out of the picture.

Thus, we have all come to realize more and more how extremely difficult it is to assign an approximately correct magnitude to a galaxy that appears on our photographs as a faint, blurry and elongated spot of very small apparent size and without any proper structure visible.

To add to our problems, we have still not solved in a satisfactory manner the difficult problem of determining total apparent magnitudes of good accuracy for the thousands upon thousands of faint galaxies that appear on our photographs. It may still take quite a few years before we accumulate observational data of sufficient reliability to permit us to plot the overall distribution in depth of the one hundred million galaxies which are now within reach of our photographic telescopes. Until this time has arrived, we had better be careful not to depend too heavily on conclusions based on statistical material on the distribution in depth of the galaxies in our universe.

Up to this point we have concerned ourselves wholly with optical data relating to the distribution of distant galaxies. The large radio telescopes and special arrays used in radio astronomy for recording faint radio radiations in the meter range suggest the presence of many remote radio sources, some of them probably way beyond the limits of distance reached by our optical surveys.

This optical limit is generally placed at a distance of the order of six thousand million light years from the Sun. About two thousand extra-galactic radio sources have been charted, notably by B. Y. Mills of the University of Sydney and by Martin Ryle at the Cavendish Laboratory. The brightest of this variety of radio source is identified as a pair of galaxies at a distance of the order of six hundred million light years from the Sun, all of which suggests that the observed radio sources that appear only one one-thousandth as strong must be very distant indeed, fully as remote as the faintest galaxy observed by optical means.

At present, radio-source surveys suffer also from difficulties with brightness estimates, but the principal source of trouble lies in the fact that we have no direct way of estimating distances. The only approach to the distance problem is through optical identification of the radio source with an object of known distance, and hence the radio-source distances are even less well determined than the distances of galaxies. However, statistical results on frequencies of radio sources have already contributed some important conclusions with regard to the structure of the universe of galaxies. Ryle at the Cavendish Laboratory, and Mills in

Sydney, have studied the rate at which the number of radio sources (most of them of extra-galactic origin) increases with decreasing radio brightness, and both are agreed that the rate of increase is faster than one would expect for a steady-state universe of constant density. Before we point to the most likely explanation of this observed fact, we should remind the reader that in extra-galactic astronomy we are not only looking at objects at great distances, but we are observing these as they were thousands of millions of years ago. In other words, we are looking back in time. The observed piling up of faint radio sources at great distances probably means that we are observing them at a time in the past history of the Universe when explosions leading to radio emission (supernova star explosions to some extent) were more frequent than they are now. Hence we see proportionally more radio sources at distances of 5000 million light years than we do near us, since the faint radio sources are, in fact, radio reports of cosmic events that took place 5000 million years ago. The apparent piling up of radio sources at great distances is obviously suggestive of an evolutionary Universe rather than a steady-state Universe.

The evolutionary Universe of which we are a part is almost certainly a truly expanding Universe. None of the researches of the past decade has thrown any doubts about the reality of the expansion of the universe of galaxies. One of the most notable observational accomplishments of the past few years has been R. Minkowski's measurement of a red shift equal to 46 per cent of the speed of light (138,000 km/sec) for a galaxy at an estimated distance of 6000 million light years from the Sun.

To what extent, we may well ask, do uncertainties in estimated distances of galaxies affect our thinking concerning the expanding Universe and related problems? As the final result of any observational analysis involving red shifts and distances of galaxies, astronomers quote generally the Hubble Constant, which gives the derived expansion rate in kilometres per second for a distance of one million parsecs from the Sun. Since one parsec equals 3·26 light years (one parsec is the distance for a star with parallax of one second of arc), the Hubble Constant represents the expansion rate at a distance of three million two hundred and sixty thousand light years. With modern observational techniques, the red shifts, and hence the velocities of recession, may be measured with very low percentage errors, and most of the uncertainty lies in the estimated distance. To the best of my knowledge, no astronomer subscribes any more to the value $H = 300$, often quoted in the past. Five years ago the value $H = 150$ seemed a fair one, but considerably lower values have been advocated during the past two or three years, with

H = 100 the most likely value and H = 75 not at all outside the realm of possibility. The precise value of the Hubble Constant is of great importance to all theorists who deal with problems of an expanding evolutionary Universe, since in most models the derived basic Expansion Age of the Universe is inversely proportional to the assumed value of the Hubble Constant. Assuming a more or less constant expansion rate, the Expansion Age turns out to be about eight thousand million years for H = 100, whereas for H = 150 the corresponding expansion age would be only five thousand million years. The quoted values of the expansion age depend on the model of the Universe employed in these calculations; a value of eight to ten thousand million years has become generally accepted. It is obviously of the greatest significance that we should attempt to obtain precise information about the distances of the remote galaxies, but unfortunately this task is far from simple.

In the evolutionary Universe the expansion age represents the true age since the formation of our Universe and the start of the general expansion. The quantity would, of course, have no meaning in the steady-state Universe advocated by Hoyle, Bondi and Gold, which universe would have no beginning, no end and no boundary. But these are questions beyond the scope of this section which is supposed to deal primarily with observational problems.

One might ask if there is perhaps any suggestion, in the observations, of a non-uniformity in the general expansion. Conflicting views are currently held on this point and it is my considered opinion that it is not safe to make any firm pronouncements on this score at the present time.

In the past there have been several suggestions that the expansion of the Universe is only an apparent one and that the observed phenomena may be explained in some other manner. Support for hypotheses that explain the observed phenomena through processes different from a general expansion has gradually ceased. Not only does it seem as though all of the optical data fit nicely into the expansion picture, but all available radio astronomical evidence points in the same direction.

For the present, we may therefore rest relatively assured that the expansion of our Universe of galaxies is a real phenomenon, to be reckoned with in all theoretical research.

CHAPTER 9

The Solar System – Its Construction and Composition

Introduction

It seems clear to most people that researches into our astronomical neighbourhood, the solar system, have entered a new phase. We have looked through telescopes at the Moon and the planets for a very long time now and it seems that almost all the data of value that could be gathered by these techniques have by now been obtained. The available techniques have been stretched to the utmost and, although there has been much interest in the solar system during the last fifty years, there has been little progress in methods of investigation.

In recent years the outlook has changed completely. We can now contemplate freeing ourselves from many of the restrictions that have hampered work in the past. The interference of our own atmosphere need not be tolerated any longer; observations of greater clarity and in wave bands outside those transmitted by the atmosphere are now possible. The interplanetary gas is directly accessible to observation by instruments and thus all quantities like density, streaming velocities, strengths of magnetic fields carried by the gas, and fluxes of energetic particles churning through this gas, are measureable. The enigmatic surface of the Moon most probably contains a record of the history of the solar system; a record which has long ago been obliterated on Earth through the violence of the geological processes here. Instead of the many interpretations of the lunar surface that are apparently permissible when it can only be seen with the resolution of a terrestrial telescope, we shall find the correct interpretation and the method of reading a long record when instruments, and one day people, can roam the lunar surface.

No one can yet say what information will be found from the surface of Mars and Venus when these come under direct investigation by instruments landed there. Mars seems to hold out the magnificent promise of giving us the most important clues concerning the origin of life.

With this new phase of research just commencing, it is interesting to speculate what solutions of major problems are likely. Since the days of Copernicus and Galileo, when the nature of the solar system was more or less understood, the question of its origin has been one of the outstanding scientific problems. Unless the problem is much harder than we think, the new techniques should solve it.

The various steps of this space research, when they happen, will undoubtedly be highly publicized. It seems to me that this gives astronomers an obligation to try to prepare the ground as far as the public is concerned, and to make clear where discussion of the problem has led to at the present time, so that each new step when it comes can be evaluated and understood, not only in astronomical circles, but by the interested public.

Theories of the origin of the solar system have been discussed for 150 years now. The ideas of Laplace, that a nebula surrounded the Sun and condensed into planets, is still very close to the mainstream of the modern discussion, although by now we can be much more specific in many respects and we also recognize major difficulties of which Laplace was unaware. There were also the theories in which not only the Sun and the surrounding gas cloud were involved but also a second star which served in a variety of ways to bring about the circumstances that were thought to be necessary to account for the situation. The understanding of the importance of magnetic forces in gas masses on this scale now seems to make it unnecessary to look to the more complex mechanisms, and I think that in recent times there has been a shift back, therefore, to the point of view that no more than the history of a star like the Sun should be invoked to build the planetary system.

The two main features which it is thought must be accounted for by the correct origin theory are the distribution of the chemical elements in the various planets and the sharing out of the angular momentum of the system. It was in this last respect that the intervention of another star seemed for a long time very desirable, for it is necessary to account for the possession by 1 tenth of 1 per cent of the mass of the system, of 98 per cent of the angular momentum. The planets representing only one thousandth of the mass of the Sun move in orbits so far around the Sun that they possess almost all the angular momentum of the system, leaving only 2 per cent in the spin of the Sun around its axis. Once the planets are concentrated objects, as they are now, no forces can be found that could significantly alter the distribution of the angular momentum. It is therefore clear that this distribution must have been set up in an earlier phase of the system when the material was more finely divided and could for that reason be subjected to other types of force. A disc of gas and dust, for example, would be subject to hydrodynamic, and as we now understand, magnetic forces.

Such forces may have shaped the gaseous disc and distributed the material and angular momentum in the required way before the condensation process that made the planets took place.

Researches with the aid of space vehicles into the dynamical and magnetic properties of the gas which is at the present time in the solar system will lead to an understanding of the phenomena that could have taken place in an earlier phase.

The processes that led to the chemical separation which undoubtedly distinguishes the different planets from each other, and which led to their agglomeration, can probably be understood when lunar samples become available. To realize the significance of the new information let us now look in more detail at the present knowledge, and at the present theories of the solar system.

The Main Construction and Composition

All the orbits of the planets demonstrate the common direction of the angular momentum. Apart from small perturbations the orbits are, of course, all plane and closed, and all but two are in planes within $3\frac{1}{2}$ degrees of one another. The spins of almost all the planets around their own axes also reflect this common direction though not quite so strongly. Starting from inside, nearest the Sun, we have first Mercury, which has ceased rotating relative to the Sun, so that the same face is permanently turned towards it. Next comes Venus, whose rotation has not yet been observed on account of the constant cloud cover which allows no reference marks to be seen. Next is the Earth, whose spin is in the same direction as its orbital motion, but with the axis of the spin inclined $23\frac{1}{2}$ degrees to the axis of the orbit. Next comes Mars with rather similar circumstances, with a period of revolution similar to that of the Earth, namely 24 hours 37 minutes and with its axis tipped by 25 degrees. Next is Jupiter rotating once in 11 hours, again in the same direction with the axis tipped by 3 degrees. Then comes Saturn, rotating once in 10 hours, inclined by 27 degrees. Next are the medium-sized planets, Uranus and Neptune and lastly, the smaller Pluto. Amongst these, the ones out of step are Uranus, whose axis of rotation is tipped over to lie approximately in the plane of its orbit, and Pluto, revolving in an orbit which is inclined some 17 degrees to the plane of most others, and which is quite markedly elliptical and not nearly circular like the remainder. There are some thirty satellites associated with all these planets and most of them also go around in the same forward direction, and in planes that are closely related to the equatorial planes of the parent planet.

It is obvious that the system has a very large tendency for regularity and that the source of the angular momentum must have been a common one. On the other hand, some significant disturbing tendencies must have been present to give the observed scatter to the data.

The terrestrial planets, that is Mercury, Venus, Earth and Mars, and the asteroids mainly located in the belt beyond Mars, are thought to be composed mostly of the types of materials that the Earth is composed of, though in somewhat different proportions. Iron, oxygen, magnesium, silicon, probably make up some 90 per cent of them all. The situation is quite different for the major planets Jupiter and Saturn, where hydrogen is probably the main constituent and other light elements helium, carbon, nitrogen, oxygen, neon, probably contribute most of the remainder. Uranus and Neptune are probably also composed largely of the light elements, but do not contain nearly as great an abundance of hydrogen. There is great uncertainty about Pluto, since estimates of its mass and radius give results for its density that are rather improbable.

Estimates of the composition of bodies other than the Earth have been derived mainly from a knowledge of the density of the material. There is, however, another source of information which has been of very great significance in discussion of the origin of the solar system, and that is the meteorites. Meteorites that fall on to the Earth and that are big enough to penetrate the atmosphere and are subsequently found lying on the ground, provide a whole host of pieces of information concerning the circumstances that must have existed at another place at another time. It is difficult to be sure that the samples investigated are really representative ones, for it is much easier to find the iron meteorites than the stony ones which are more easily confused with local materials. The estimates are that some 90 per cent of all meteorites are stony, about 10 per cent are a nickel–iron alloy, and a very few are roughly half nickel–iron, half silicate. The majority of the stony meteorites are quite different from the rocks on the Earth's surface. They tend to contain fine veins of nickel–iron alloy and they also have a remarkably high magnesium, and a low aluminium and alkali, content. The terrestrial rocks that most closely approach the composition of these meteorites are very deep-seated ones. There is, however, a big difference in the structure, for most of these meteorites contain small rounded silicate grains – so-called chondrules – embedded in a mixture of other substances including broken chondrules and materials that must have been liquid at one time. About 10 per cent of the stony meteorites lack this structure and a large fraction of these is, in turn, peculiar in being almost free from metal and possessing far more calcium and aluminium that the typical meteorites and therefore being much more similar to rocks on the Earth's crust.

The wealth of information that can be deduced from their physical and chemical structure is quite astounding. All investigators of meteorites agree that the chondritic meteorites must be the result of a melting process followed by cooling and a violent break-up, followed by a reaccumulation into the final object. In some cases a very gradual cooling process can be shown to be required for the crystallographic configurations.

In addition to the thermal and physical history of these objects, it is possible to determine their age by radioactivity measurements. One method is based on the ratio of lead isotopes and radioactive uranium isotopes. Another method is based on the ratio of potassium-40 to argon-40, and another on the amount of helium left over in the specimen as a result of the decay of radioactive uranium and thorium. Each of these methods will determine the age of the sample since it was last hot enough to make possible the escape of some elements. This is, in detail, different for the different methods and for different specimens, but nevertheless it is clear from the results that a large fraction of the material has been undisturbed for a period of 3 to $4\frac{1}{2}$ thousand million years, and that before that time it had been hot and possibly molten. Urey has discussed all these data in relation to the theories of the origin of the solar system and we shall return to some of these points later. The outstanding conclusion from all the investigations of meteorites is undoubtedly that these objects must have been part of one or more major bodies before being distributed on their individual orbits by some violent events.

CHAPTER 10

The Cold Accumulation Theory of the Solar System

There is such a great deal of information concerning the solar system, any of which may be relevant to a theory of its origin, that it would be impossibly dull just to go through it all, item by item. A more interesting way is to select a particular theory and then discuss the evidence in favour of or against it. With the brief outline we have from the previous chapter, we shall therefore now plunge into theory. I have naturally selected the one that I think has the best chance of success. It is one whose first beginnings date back to the writings of Chamberlain and Moulton, about fifty years ago, who called their theory the Planetesimal. Many scientists have since contributed to this basic line of thought, according to which an initial accumulation happened from small solid particles that had condensed out of a gaseous disc. The origin of the gaseous disc is uncertain. It may have occurred during the process of condensation of the Sun from interstellar gas, but there is the difficulty concerning the angular momentum being so unevenly distributed between the different masses. Why, in the condensation process, should the piece that has 99·9 per cent of the mass only get 2 per cent of the angular momentum? One could perhaps understand this if the condensation process of the Sun were in any way limited by angular momentum, that is if the body were spinning so fast that this prevented the material from condensing. But with the present rotation speed of the Sun this could not have been true. The present Sun could be spinning fifty times faster and its spin would still be quite insignificant dynamically.

Theories that involve a second star for the creation of the gaseous disc have to appeal to some substantial improbabilities, for even if a close encounter between two stars or an actual collision were envisaged, the dynamics of the situation make it very unlikely that so much angular momentum would go into some of the ejected material. Also, if a second star had been responsible, the fact that the Sun's axis and sense of rotation is rather similar to that of the bulk of the planetary disc would be a complete coincidence. One therefore felt inclined to see whether some process could not occur that would take angular momentum from an originally fast spinning sun and put this into the gaseous disc, thereby spreading it out to the dimensions now possessed by the solar system.

Such a point of view derives support from a very interesting astronomical observation. It is known, through spectroscopic examination of the light from other stars, that stars rotate at very different speeds. Now it looks as if the rotation speeds are not just randomly distributed amongst the stars but as if, instead, there are two definite classes: the fast rotating and the slowly rotating stars. These two classes show a correlation with another characteristic of the stars, namely their colour. The blue stars tend to be fast rotators and the redder stars tend to be slow rotators. The division between the two classes occurs at stars a little bluer than the Sun. What is it that determines the rotation speeds of the stars and what has caused this division?

One used to think that there was nothing that could change the rotation speed of a star once this star was formed, and therefore that this speed must depend entirely on the original angular momentum possessed by the gaseous cloud from which the star was formed. If we look at gas masses in the galaxy, and see what quantity of angular momentum is possessed by masses of gas of the right order to form a star, then almost invariably we come to rather high values. In most cases a star so formed would be spinning much faster than the observed stars and indeed so fast that its gravitational field would fail to hold it together. That, of course, does not mean that it would form and then burst, but merely that these gases could never form the star. One thus thought that, in the star formation process, gas masses must be selected rather carefully so as not to exceed the maximum permissible angular momentum. That would merely mean, of course, that there would be many false starts and comparatively few successes in this formation process. In that case, however, the vast majority of the stars ought to be spinning very close to their maximum speed. On this basis one clearly cannot explain the existence of a large class of stars that rotate so slowly that this rotation is dynamically completely insignificant for them. So even without the solar system in mind, one would have wanted to discuss processes that could rob a star once formed of most of its angular momentum and put it into some form in which we could not observe it. We might for this reason alone have suspected that most stars like the Sun are, in fact, associated with some masses to which they have given most of their angular momentum.

These observations therefore contain the suggestion that all stars started life, as one would have expected, as fast rotators, but that in all stars except those much bluer than the Sun a process then occurred that distributed the angular momentum mostly into a planetary disc. If this were so, then the majority of stars might have planets. This is something that I think would interest us greatly.

In recent years the study of magnetic fields in tenuous gases has made substantial progress and one now understands the great significance that these fields have for the dynamics of the interstellar gas. These forces may indeed provide a sufficiently strong coupling between a star and a gaseous disc surrounding it to slow up the star significantly in its lifetime.

The following set of events may therefore have occurred. Firstly, a star condensed out of the interstellar gas possessing, as one might expect, an excessive amount of angular momentum. This formed the Sun, spinning then near the limiting speed, but leaving over substantial amounts of gas that possessed too much angular momentum to join the body of the Sun. This gas would then be rotating around the Sun fairly close to it. But being farther from the centre of rotation, its angular velocity would be less than the Sun although per unit mass it contained more angular momentum. If there were any force that acted like a friction between the Sun's surface and the surrounding medium, then such a force would tend to push in the direction of the rotation of the gas, and would therefore supply more angular momentum to it, taking it away from the Sun.

These dynamical situations are not always quite easy to understand. We might think of the familiar Earth – Moon System as an example. The Moon possesses more angular momentum per unit mass around the axis of rotation of the system than the Earth does. But because it is further from its axis it takes twenty-eight days to go around instead of one, like the material of the Earth. If now we imagine the Earth to possess a huge atmosphere so extended that it reaches as far as the Moon, then there could be a frictional interaction between the two bodies. Friction would make the atmosphere of the Earth rotate with the Earth, that is, once in twenty-four hours; and the Moon rotating much more slowly, would therefore be pushed from behind. This, perversely, would not make the Moon go any faster around the Earth, for it would only take up an orbit still farther away, whose revolution period would be even longer. Pushing an orbiting mass from behind makes it take longer to go around, and applying a brake to its motion makes it go around in a shorter time.

A revolving gaseous mass around the Sun would therefore continue to gain angular momentum from any frictional coupling with the Sun and it would then revolve on larger and larger orbits. The important point is that gas dynamics as discussed in the past failed to provide the possibility of an adequate frictional coupling. Magnetohydrodynamics, that is the study of conducting gases in magnetic fields, however, seems to provide this possibility. Magnetic fields such as the ones we now know to exist on the solar surface may stretch out from the Sun and exert significant forces on the surrounding gas. Over periods of hundreds of millions of years, this effect could be significant and could have resulted in the present distribution of angular momentum.

How can a conjecture of this sort ever be checked? Of course, it is not likely that we shall have an opportunity to watch the formation of any other solar system, but we may have an opportunity to observe the same kind of forces still at work today. The quantity of gas now left in the solar system is, of course, a great deal less than that which must have been there to provide the building material of the planets. Even so, there is some gas, and it may be possible to measure its state of motion and the magnetic fields it carries. It would be possible to deduce from such measurements, which may be carried out with the aid of instrumented space vehicles, whether the Sun is at the present time still shedding angular momentum. We would not be able to see more than the very tail end of this process, but even so it might still be possible to recognize clearly all its features. Therefore, by a remarkable argument, such a measurement of the present-day conditions of the interplanetary gas would tell us whether we are to expect the great majority of stars to possess planetary systems. If magnetic friction is at work, then there are probably more than 10^{10} planetary systems in our galaxy alone. These measurements could be one of the high spots of space research in the very near future.

Now we must turn to the question of the physical and chemical processes that might occur in the gaseous disc. Being distributed to great distances, the outer parts would receive very little solar heat, and would therefore cool down to very low temperatures. At these temperatures of only a few tens of degrees absolute, many molecules would, of course, be formed, and these in turn would make up solid objects. The solar composition, and therefore also that of this gas, is very largely hydrogen, with the light elements, carbon, nitrogen, oxygen making up a large fraction of the remainder. Materials as heavy as silicon or iron in atomic weight are only present in concentrations of the order of $0\cdot1$ per cent. In the cold outer regions by far the most abundant solids that would form would be substances like ice, solid ammonia, methane, and other combinations of the light elements. Closer in towards the Sun, where the temperatures are higher, only the more refractory materials could go into a solid form and make small particles. The gaseous disc would therefore develop a distribution, graded according to vapour pressure and abundance, of little solid dust particles, and the next stages would depend critically on their surface properties. Small dust particles would be moving exactly with the gas. When perchance neighbouring particles came to touch each other, they would very likely do this at a very low relative velocity and might then easily stick together if the surfaces were slightly adhesive. This, of course, is very much like the formation of snow flakes which grow together by such chance encounters. Snowballs of the light element ices would form far out in the system, and agglomerates of various chemical combinations of the heavier elements like silicon and iron that tend to make refractory materials would form in the inner part.

What would happen to these agglomerations? How many of them would form? And would they sweep up all the initial small grains?

Individual agglomerations would grow until they had significantly depleted the density of grains in their vicinity. Neighbouring agglomerations would, of course, compete for material and larger and larger agglomerations would form both by picking up individual grains and by picking up other smaller agglomerates. When bodies of the order of some miles across had been formed their gravitational attraction would become important and they would be able to grab much more material than would have come into contact with their surface otherwise. This, then, constitutes a race for the survival of the biggest, for those that are bigger can grow faster. A number of major bodies would therefore form, proceeding around the Sun on keplerian orbits, but perturbing each other significantly. Every now and again two major pieces would collide with one another and get partly scattered again in this collision. New agglomeration would then happen, and new collisions for long periods of time. In all this process of agglomeration and collision energy would be dissipated, for heat would be produced and radiated away. It is clear, therefore, that the process could not go on indefinitely. The source of the energy is, of course, the gravitational potential energy released by the formation of the massive bodies and, therefore, a loss of energy from the entire system must correspond to a growth of those bodies.

Of course, bodies that were formed on orbits very far from one another could never collide and therefore there would be a process akin to one of natural selection in which those bodies that were not on possible collision orbits with others large enough to destroy them would be the eventual survivors. In other words the system would sort itself out and bigger bodies would grow, each on a lane that it dominated, and collisions would become rarer and rarer as time goes on.

In a system that had formed in this way, it is clear that there would be a lot of order but not complete perfection. All the major bodies would necessarily still be going around in the same direction, for the collisions would always have been with objects going around in that same direction. The collection of the originally finely divided material would always tend to make for regularity in the objects so formed; the plane of the orbit would have a small inclination, the axis of spin would be normal to the plane, and the eccentricity of the orbit would be small. Then, however, when major collisions and perturbations occurred, some irregularity would be produced. The spin angular momentum which would be given to a body by such a collision is obviously quite arbitrary, since it would depend on the precise place of the impact, and it would therefore not be surprising that the spin axes should all have been knocked about somewhat by these processes. In fact, the remaining level of regularity allows one to estimate that the planets have been put together in their final form with only a small fraction of the mass added in large lumps, and most in small pieces. This does not say, of course, whether these small pieces were mostly the original dust grains or shattered pieces from any of the many preceding collision processes.

There are many points in this general scheme which need to be argued out in considerable detail. For example, why did the two major planets, Jupiter and Saturn, become so enormous? Why are there so many satellites? Why is the Moon so much less dense than the Earth?

If the original material of the gaseous disc was of approximately the same composition as the Sun and most of the stars, then it is clear that by now the planetary system has lost a great deal of hydrogen and has therefore concentrated the heavier elements. Jupiter and Saturn, however, have a large proportion of hydrogen, and this could be understood if they were formed in the way we have discussed, mostly by the agglomeration of light element ices, at a time when a lot of this hydrogen was still here. Once the bodies had reached a certain size, their gravitational field and the rather low temperature would have allowed a hydrogen atmosphere to be accumulated. The inner planets could never do this however much hydrogen there was around, for their gravitational field is not strong enough and the temperature at this distance from the Sun is high so that the hydrogen would readily escape. But Jupiter and Saturn could sweep up more and more hydrogen and indeed this would only increase the mass and therefore the gravitational field of the planet, and therefore accelerate the sweeping up of more. The amount that was swept up must therefore relate to the amount that was there and within their grasp, so to speak. Uranus and Neptune farther out would, of course, have had the same possibility, and the fact that they did not bloat themselves with hydrogen, but remained bodies largely composed of elements like carbon, nitrogen, and oxygen, must mean that on their orbits there was not much hydrogen available. Perhaps at this great distance hydrogen gas was too weakly bound in the solar gravitational field and it could escape into space either through its own thermal motion or through the sweeping and heating action of the interstellar gas through which the whole solar system must constantly be ploughing, at speeds of the order of a few kilometres per second. It is not at all unreasonable that there should be a cut off to the distance at which a hydrogen cloud could be held by the Sun for long periods of time.

The existence of so many satellites whose orbits are closely related to the spin of the parent planet strongly suggests that some frictional force between the planet and the satellite material was in existence at one time. It is only by the operation of a quite unreasonable amount of chance that satellites could be formed without the intervention of a resisting medium, and so for this reason alone one would have to think that enormously more gaseous matter had been present at one time than we now have. Very likely large amounts of hydrogen, some tens of times more than the total mass of the planets, were responsible for this.

The Earth, as we have said, could not hold a hydrogen atmosphere. But, on the other hand, if the whole region of the solar system in which the Earth moves contained a lot of hydrogen, then the Earth's gravitational field would make a very substantial concentration. Any particular hydrogen atom might be acquired and lost again in this atmosphere, but the density would be high. Most of such a hydrogen atmosphere would rotate with the planet and it is in such circumstances that small particles could be captured into orbits encircling the planet. Such particles in turn would make agglomerations and collisions, and from there on the story is much the same as it was on the larger scale for the formation of the planets around the Sun. It is significant that no case occurs in which the angular momentum contained in the satellites is so great that one could not suppose it to have come from the planet. If the angular momentum of the satellites were put back into the planets, no planet would be rotating at bursting speed.

We all know that a satellite revolving around the Earth at a small distance takes about $1\frac{1}{2}$ hours for a revolution. If it is moving in the region where there are still atmospheric gases revolving with the Earth, then there is some friction and the force applied to the satellite is in the sense of opposing its motion. The change in the orbit that results, brings the satellite closer to the Earth and diminishes the length of its period. Eventually, of course, it crashes to the Earth. This, however, is not the situation at all heights. If there were still a significant amount of atmospheric drag at a height of twenty-six thousand miles, then the sense of the result would be reversed. A satellite encircling the Earth at this height has the property of taking just exactly twenty-four hours to revolve once. There would then be no friction with any gases which, rotating with the Earth, take just the same time. For any particles a little farther out than this distance a frictional drag would work in the opposite sense. It would push them in the direction in which they are going and it would therefore lead to larger orbits possessing more angular momentum. For the example of the present Earth, this critical level is rather high for there to be in reality any significant atmospheric drag. But the primitive Earth would have revolved very much faster, because it had not yet distributed so much angular momentum to the Moon, and correspondingly the critical point would have been very much lower.

Though at the present time none of these processes can be very effective any more, it might still be worthwhile examining whether there are any streams of dust grains encircling the Earth in the vicinity of this critical height. If even a trace of these were found, a sort of very weak Saturn's ring, this would strengthen the case for such a mode of origin of the Moon.

In the planetary system we have one case where the process of collision and accumulation has not yet been brought to its final conclusion. The belt of asteroids between Mars and Jupiter is a region in which collisions must still be happening, in which energy therefore is still being dissipated, and in which a change to a different configuration must still be taking place. For the satellite system we have another case of a similar sort, namely the rings of Saturn. These, it is known, must be composed of small pieces, and again processes of collision and accumulation must be occurring.

The situation to which the solar system must be tending is one in which no further collisions can occur. This, it can be shown, is one in which there are only planets going around in orbits sufficiently far from one another so that no large perturbations can occur. Each planet must have a clear lane assigned to it all around the orbit. An object like the Moon cannot be going around somewhere else on the lane assigned to the Earth without eventually coming into collision; this, of course, does not prevent the Moon from going around together with the Earth on a satellite orbit. Each planet may possess satellites without risking collision. Thus the demand for a collision-free system with the motions nearly confined to a common plane is already enough to specify something that looks quite a bit like the planetary and satellite system.

CHAPTER 11

The Structure and Evolution of the Earth

We should now discuss whether the huge amount of evidence we have concerning the Earth is in agreement with the mode of origin we have outlined. The processes that occur in the interior of a largely solid body like the Earth are sufficiently slow not to have reached their final conclusion. This means that the present construction still contains a lot of evidence concerning the earlier phases. This would not be true, for example, if it had gone through a period where it was all molten and in which, therefore, any evidence relating to an earlier time would have been destroyed. This does not, however, seem to have been the case.

The construction of the Earth as it is known from seismic evidence is crudely speaking in three layers (Fig. 11.1). On the top there is a crust of very variable thickness, some 50 to 100 km thick where the continents are, and possibly only 10 km or less under the oceans. This crust is composed of a material of considerably lower density than all that is below. The mean density of the crust is about 2·8 g/cc and the density of the material just below is probably in the neighbourhood of 3·3 g/cc. The mean density of the entire mantle is about 4·5 g/cc. Within the porous mantle liquids are assumed to drain upwards or downwards, depending on their density. The upward draining material is impeded by the layer at which freezing would occur, and can get through it only where the flow is fast enough to maintain a higher temperature. Then, below all this, the innermost part (approximately half of the Earth's radius and therefore an eighth of the volume) appears to be a liquid core with a density a little in excess of 10 g/cc. The interpretation which is usually given is that the thin crust is composed of a particularly light variety of silicate rocks, while the mantle below is made of the heaviest silicates containing iron and magnesium, possibly also iron sulphide as well as perhaps some metallic nickel–iron. The liquid core is thought to be made of iron and nickel, just because these are the abundant elements that would be expected to liquefy sooner than the dense silicates, and they would possess approximately the correct density. How could a body like this have been put together? By the accumulation of big and small pieces in the manner we have discussed?

Many authors in the past have discussed the internal constitution of the Earth on the basis that it must at one time have been all liquid. On the other hand there never has existed a theory argued out in physical detail for a way of condensing a body as small as the Earth in a hot condition, as was mostly implied in these discussions. The very patchy distribution of the lighter continental material argues heavily against there

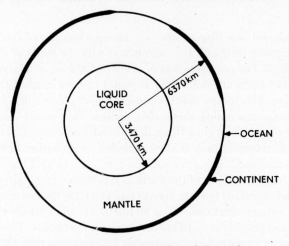

Fig. 11.1. The three layer construction of the earth

ever having been complete liquefaction, for in that case one could not understand why the materials of different density did not distribute themselves in the hydrostatic equilibrium of a set of spherical shells. The continental masses clearly need substantial forces of rigidity to hold the continents together and prevent them from flowing out over the surface into a uniform layer.

Much of the tendency to regard the Earth as having been originally liquid has no doubt come from the geological evidence which shows that a very major fraction, if not all, of the material that is now on the Earth's surface has once been liquid. But there are other ways, as we shall see, in which such a state of affairs could have come about.

Chamberlain and Moulton in the U.S.A. and also Schmidt in the U.S.S.R. have discussed the physically much more acceptable alternative of a condensation of the Earth from cold small particles as it would have occurred in the solar system formation process which we have discussed. Their discussion can, in fact, be extended to show how a great many of the known facts about the Earth may be expected to result from such a beginning.

If we think of an Earth growing by an accumulation process of small particles interspersed with a few big ones, it is clear that the interior would not be entirely homogenous, for the different regions would have suffered different treatment as a consequence of the major impacts. At any stage during growth the surface would have been pitted with a large number of impact craters in a way perhaps not very different from the present surface of the Moon. As more and more material was piled on some heating would have occurred in the interior for three different reasons. Firstly, the impacts would result in pressure waves which transported energy and some of them would get attenuated deep down in depths from whence heat conduction to the surface would be an exceedingly slow process. Secondly, as more material was piled on the top, there would have been a gradual increase of pressure inside and an amount of heat would have been released by the compression of the material in a way that depends in detail upon the relation of pressure, volume, and internal energy of the substance at these high pressures. Our knowledge of these quantities for very high pressures is inadequate and therefore the amount of heat released by this process cannot be estimated very accurately. Thirdly, there would have been the amount of heat released by the radioactive minerals which has often been discussed, but still with rather indefinite conclusions.

The loss of heat from a large body like the Earth is a remarkably small effect. Even in intervals of time like four or five thousand million years the deep interior would not cool itself significantly by heat conduction to the surface. The critical thing for an estimation of the internal temperature is therefore almost entirely the question of the amount of heat that has become available, and the greatest contribution has probably been that of the radioactivity. Although different authors have made models of the Earth's interior with certain distributions of radioactive minerals and then calculated in some detail the temperature that would result from these models, it must be admitted that the basic information still allows a wide range of possibilities. These sources of heat could easily amount to what is necessary to heat the interior to temperatures of perhaps 4000° or 5000°K. Probably the best estimate that can be made at the present time of the internal temperatures is based on the knowledge that at the core–mantle interface the temperature must be suitable to allow the solid mantle and the liquid core to co-exist. The melting-point of most substances increases with pressure and it has been estimated that iron would be liquid at a temperature in excess of about 4500°K. On the other hand, in order to retain the solid phase of the other materials, the heavy silicates, in the inner part of the mantle, the temperature would probably have to be lower than about 7000°K. As we go upward from the core, the melting-points of the substances decrease as the pressure decreases but equally the amount of heat supplied diminishes somewhat because the contribution from the compressional effect becomes less important; and as we approach the surface, the amount of heat lost to the exterior increases.

The heterogeneous collection of materials that may make up the Earth have the property that over quite a wide range of temperatures a certain fraction but not all, would be in a liquid state. This range of temperatures is wide enough for it to be quite plausible that the whole solid mantle could be in this condition. Near the top we know, after all, that the lowest-melting-point substances, namely certain light silicates, can exist as lava. In the deep interior we believe that liquid iron can occur. Yet the seismic evidence is perfectly definite in showing that the entire mantle is capable of transmitting transverse seismic waves and therefore is in the main solid. This, however, does not prove that it is not pervaded by veins of liquid of the light or the heavy sort, whose seismic effects would be small.

If we imagined a heterogeneous collection of substances to be heated

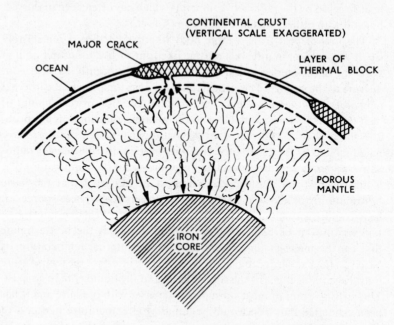

Fig. 11.2. The pore theory of the Earth's interior. Schematic illustration of the interior structure

up gradually until a certain fraction of the material is liquid, then at a certain stage enough communication between the liquid parts would occur for a migration to be possible. In actual fact, the big earthquakes connected with the major impacts would probably have helped greatly to allow a small liquid fraction to establish communicating channels. Perhaps we may anticipate here a point that will come up again later: the structure of the meteorites, we have said, proves that they have once been parts of some major bodies and they indeed show a structure which, for the most part, must have resulted from the combination of metallic and silicate liquid veins pervading a solid agglomerate. Perhaps we see in them representative cases of the kind of structure that is set up in the interior of a terrestrial planet.

Once the growing Earth had heated to internal temperatures at which some communicating liquid channels exist, gravitational sorting of materials would have taken place. The much heavier liquid iron would have drained towards what is the centre, distending the metal veins lower down and allowing the ones higher up to contract. The mean density of the material would therefore increase systematically towards the centre. Eventually the inward draining metal would form a dense liquid core, such as the Earth now has. The liquid fraction, lighter than the main mass of the mantle, similarly would have a tendency to rise upwards. One might think that it would then be expected to come up to the surface and make a layer of low-melting-point light material there. There is however, an added complication which it is well worth discussing.

The Thermal Block

The deep interior of the Earth, below a depth of a few hundred kilometres, cannot lose much heat to the outside because of the great thermal insulation (Fig. 11.2) provided by the overlying material. The outermost layer is, however, kept quite cold by radiation into space; so cold that no structure of pores or veins of liquid constituents could exist there in the rock. The porous structure and the percolation of liquids could therefore not apply to the topmost layer, and all communication would be blocked through freezing. The lighter liquid constituents down below would be held under by being unable to penetrate the cold layer above and while this situation may be in hydrostatic equilibrium, it is certainly not stable. If any sufficiently large crack developed in the cold upper layer, then the accumulated liquid would make its way up through this crack. Now it is a very important feature of this process that a small crack would not suffice. Through a small crack there could only be a slow rate of flow and the upwelling material would soon freeze in contact with the cold solid. If, however, there was a crack which was large enough, the upward draining could continue, for then the upwelling material would bring enough heat up with it to prevent freezing. This, of course, is just the same reason as the one that causes a small water pipe to freeze up in the winter out in the open while a very large one carrying a lot of water may be quite safe.

This thermal blockage therefore assures that the light material cannot ooze out uniformly all over the Earth as would otherwise have been the natural consequence of the hydrostatic situation. Instead, it is only through some very large cracks that the light material can flow, and then once having come up through a certain crack, it will tend to keep that region hot and therefore keep the flow going there. A few major lines of upwelling must therefore be expected and this would seem to account for the existence of the continental masses distributed along a bold pattern over the globe. The light continental rock that has come up in this way cannot, of course, pile up indefinitely above the cracks out of which it has come. Its mechanical strength is inadequate to support more than a certain height and it must therefore flow out laterally once this height has been reached. A crack would therefore provide a line from which continental growth would take place.

One can see no way in which the lighter continental materials could have been put into their present places except by a gradual differentiation process from the interior. It is therefore not so much a question of whether continental growth has occurred, but rather whether it occurred during the period covered by the geological record, or whether the main bulk of the continental masses had already differentiated out in the epoch that gives us the earliest rock samples. This record is, of course, enormously complicated by the large extent to which erosion and heating processes have occurred, so that most of the material can no longer be seen in its original form, but only as a combination of sedimentary, metamorphosed, and intrusive rocks. It is of great interest in this connection that all volcanic activity is distributed in a few major lines around the globe and that those same lines are associated with mountain-building activity. It is presumably along these major crack lines that enough heat is being transported up to prevent the freezing of the lavas; volcanos and mountain building must therefore occur together. Deep down below along these lines the lighter materials are able to drain to the top and the mean density will therefore increase in the course of time. Perhaps this is the explanation of the deep ocean trenches that tend to occur close to these lines. The augmentation of the density below will, of course, lower the equilibrium position of the ocean floor. As light material pours out, the vicinity of the outpouring tends to sink.

Many geologists and geophysicists believe indeed that continental growth has occurred and is still going on. They mostly argue the case in terms of the detailed formations and their estimated ages, but there are also two overall arguments which strengthen this case. The amount of material which is being poured out as lava at the present time is by no means negligible, and it amounts to something of the order of 1 km³ per year. The total mass of continental material is not very different from 5,000,000,000 km³ which is the amount that would have been poured out at this rate since the date of formation of the oldest rocks. There are, of course, great uncertainties in this discussion, as we do not know how much of the material pouring out is merely reheated continental material and therefore ought not to appear on this balance sheet. On the other hand, there is the possibility that large quantities of continental material are contributed without ever showing up on the surface, but they merely find their way from underneath into the base of the continental blocks and thus help to lift and distend them.

If the processes that differentiate material on the Earth are still going on at the present time, one would also expect to see this in the changes suffered by the moment of inertia of the Earth. A change in the moment of inertia of the Earth will affect its rotation speed and in that way the length of day. To sort out these effects, which, of course, are very small, it is necessary to understand first what changes in the rotation speed are produced by interaction with the Moon. The Earth's rotation is slowed down by the Moon and would tend to speed up as a consequence of a differentiation of the minerals according to density. When these effects are disentangled, (as they have been in recent years by Munk and McDonald) it appears quite reasonable to suppose that the differentiation of the Earth is even now continuing at about the average rate at which it must have gone on in the past. If the Earth has an iron core, there is no reason for thinking that it has already grown to its full size. It is probably still growing as fast as ever. Similarly, there is no information that would tend to suggest that the outpouring of light materials on the top has come to an end.

CHAPTER 12

The Moon

Obliteration of Earth Features

All that we see on the surface of the Earth are the continents and the oceans. If all the continental materials are poured out from the interior then the continents cannot contain any features that relate to the preceding stages, namely, the mode of formation of the Earth. The geological record obtained almost entirely from continental material therefore has nothing to say about the appearance of the Earth in an earlier epoch. It is not known how much cover there is over the original material of the mantle in the deep oceans and it may be that there much more evidence can be obtained about the more remote past.

The Moon, as we shall discuss, has a surface that suggests heavy bombardment by big and little pieces and it has often been asked why it is, if this were the right explanation, that the Earth does not have a similar appearance. The type of continental growth we have discussed would, of course, be the answer, provided it had occurred after the bulk of the meteoritic bombardment was over. The primitive Earth, before the continents had oozed up, did perhaps have an appearance very much like the Moon with a multiple overlapping set of large and small circular markings. Can anything still be seen that relates to these markings?

The largest impacts, when they occurred, will have scooped out enormous craters to a great depth of perhaps some tens or hundreds of kilometres. Since the mechanical strength of the material could not maintain such deformations, these craters must immediately have suffered a hydrostatic adjustment that brought them all to within a kilometre or so of the level surface, and this meant that materials from underneath were squeezed up. If such impacts occurred on an earth on which a certain amount of sorting according to density had already taken place, then this sorting would have been grossly upset in the areas occupied by each of the major impacts. If we now wish to investigate what the unevennesses could have been that determined where the big cracks would develop that formed the origin of all that goes to follow, then no doubt lines of major craters or edges of big craters would be a good possibility. Now it has long been recognized that continental margins, regions of

disturbance and activity and volcanic islands in the oceans, have a large
tendency to occur on arcs of circles. I would suggest that this is all that is
still showing through of an underlying structure which, like the lunar
surface, displays the results of the huge impact events of the past.

The Moon

The first thing that must be said about the Moon is that it is completely

Fig. 12.1. The Moon aged 12½ days at 7h 24m on 28 February, 1904 (By courtesy of
the Royal Astronomical Society, London)

Fig. 12.2. Portion of the Moon at last quarter from Ptolemaeus to Tycho. 100-inch
   photograph. (By courtesy of Mount Wilson and Palomar Observatory)

different from the Earth. Firstly, there is, of course, the absence of water
and atmosphere and the consequent absence of all the erosion features
which on the Earth are due to these agencies. But even beyond that it is
quite clear that none of the great upheavals and the great distortions of
the ground that have occurred on the Earth have any counterpart on the
Moon. The Moon has no folded mountain ranges, no long chains of
volcanos, no continental blocks, no deep sea trenches. The oldest markings that are still just discernible on the lunar surface, though almost
completely obliterated by subsequent crater formation, are mostly still
nearly circular. This indicates a stability of the ground which is certainly
not possessed by the continents on the Earth. Almost anywhere on the
Earth a circle staked out one thousand million years ago would now be
exceedingly distorted. It would appear then that on the Moon none of
the processes connected with continental growth have occurred at all.

We have very little evidence about the interior of the Moon, but
know only the mean density which is 3·3 g/cc. There is no suggestion
that any core formation has taken place and therefore there is no reason
for thinking that any of the differentiation that we discussed for the

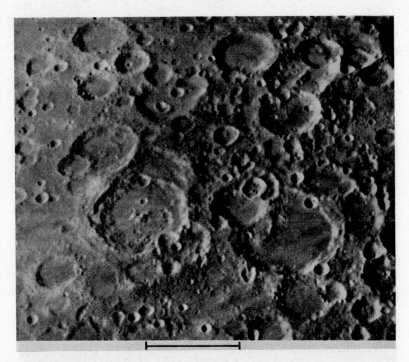

Fig. 12.3. Large magnification showing detail in densely cratered area. The line marked represents 100 km. (By courtesy of the Observatoire de Paris, Meudon)

Earth has occurred there at all. By being much smaller, the sources of internal heat of the Moon are somewhat reduced, since the pressure heating would be almost entirely absent. Also, of course, the proportion of the volume from which heat has been lost to the outside is very much greater and perhaps this is enough to account for the absence of differentiation. If a porous structure with communicating liquid veins can once get established, then it helps to keep itself going by the additional heating derived from the gravitational sorting. A lot of heat would have been liberated in the interior of the Earth in letting all the iron flow to the core, for example. So it could well be that the process is one which, above a certain threshold, could start and then go well; whereas below that threshold it could never have got going. Also, it could be that the Moon had formed later than the primitive Earth, and it may be that the radioactivity of the material had diminished considerably during the interval when the Earth was already formed, but the lunar material was still in the form of scattered particles.

If the Moon is not covered by a layer of internal origin, then clearly it will be much more favourable than the Earth for the investigation of earlier events. The geological record of the Earth refers only to the local events of extrusion of continental material and erosion. The geological record on the Moon, in which similarly a vast amount of detailed information may be found, is likely to refer to completely different processes

Fig. 12.4. The Moon: last quarter showing N.E. quadrant. 100-inch Hooker photograph. (By courtesy of Mount Wilson and Palomar Observatory)

of accumulation of material and of big impacts, namely the essential processes responsible for its own formation and that of the other bodies of the solar system. Going to the Moon and reading this geological record will, therefore, be most fascinating and instructive. The Moon may well be the body on which least change has taken place since early times and therefore not only the nearest but also the best extraterrestrial object to go to, to investigate the origin of the solar system.

If one had only seen the Earth from far away, one would probably not have thought of the vast amount of detail that can be discovered by geological exploration; of the many different physical and chemical processes that have to be explained, and of the many ways in which the age and sequence of events can be deduced once the processes are understood. 'Lunology', which is what, I suppose, lunar geology ought to be called, will probably also be a very rich subject. The physical and chemical processes will all be quite different and many of them will be processes that are much more familiar in vacuum technology than in geology. With all the physical agencies that occur there so completely different from the terrestrial ones, and with almost all formations being of a completely different type, the geologists will have no particular advantage in the subject of lunology. The subject will, in fact, have to be treated not by analogy with terrestrial processes, but at a much more basic level with which the physicist and the chemist will be much more familiar.

The exploration of the Moon by instrumented landings without people will probably be able to settle some of the major issues. With such instruments including television systems, grappling arms, and physical and chemical analysis apparatus all on a tracked vehicle and with all instrumentation controlled and reporting by radio, one will probably now be able to find out whether indeed the present features relate to big impacts in an earlier stage of the solar system. But, of course, very much more than that will be done when people go there and actually roam over the surface, and dig and look and measure and examine in any of the many ways that seems appropriate to a particular situation. How much detail one will then be able to reconstruct of the origin of the solar system is hard to say, but one will surely be able to settle the main outline and the types of processes that were involved.

The Lunar Surface

Let us now see where the discussion stands before all this great new information becomes available. The Moon's surface as seen through a good telescope can be resolved to a definition of about half a kilometre and any detail finer than that cannot be seen. With this definition several things are immediately apparent. Firstly, there is the pronounced absence of colour; the regions are mostly just different shades of grey. Secondly, it is clear that in a rough way the surface can be divided into two types (Fig. 12.4); the generally lighter, rougher ground, that seems mostly to be somewhat elevated and has therefore been called highlands, and the very much smoother, flatter, darker ground, mostly in the interior of circular regions that have been called the maria (at a time when they were thought to be seas, because of their flatness). We know, of course, that there is no significant atmosphere and no water covering any of the Moon's surface and all that we see must be different forms of the solid ground.

The other striking fact that can immediately be seen concerns the great number of circular markings called craters (Fig. 12.2), which span a huge range of sizes from several hundred kilometres, in which case they are called maria, to tens or hundreds of thousands of the size that can only just be discerned, that is, 1 or 2 km across. These craters form an unbroken distribution over the whole range of sizes although, of course, there are only very few examples of the very biggest. One is tempted, therefore, to search for one type of explanation for the whole range. There has been much discussion for a long time as to the origin of these features, but now most scientists seem to agree that this is what would be expected from impacts. For a long time a volcanic theory was favoured, but a large amount of detail could clearly not be accommodated into that theory at all. It is clear that some kind of explosion is involved and with the volcanic theory it was thought that this originated in the interior. Very large and shallow craters cannot be explained in that way, for they need an extremely intense explosion located at a shallow depth. The bottling up of internal pressures can never achieve this, for the strength of the explosion can only be what it takes to remove the overlaying material. Any such crater must always form with steep internal sides. There are many other objections to the volcanic theory as well.

Impacts, on the other hand, would provide just the kind of explosive action required. At velocities in excess of a few kilometres a second – and these are the kind of velocities that would be involved for objects pursuing slightly different orbits in the solar system – a great deal of heat would be generated at the impact. The incoming object would be completely vaporized when it had travelled a distance that is only slightly more than its own length into the ground. The subsequent effect would then be due mostly to the violent expansion of these dense and hot gases. A crater would be excavated by this explosion which is much larger than the incoming object and this immediately makes clear two of the observed features. Firstly, it is possible to obtain an extremely strong explosion whose origin is very close to the surface, just by having the velocities of the incoming objects sufficiently high (and no unreasonable velocities are, in fact, implied). As the strength of surface explosions is increased, the depth of the resulting craters will not increase as fast as the radius, and large craters will therefore be comparatively shallow, as is indeed the case. Secondly, it is clear that the direction from which the incoming object approaches the ground is almost irrelevant to the shape of the crater formed: it will in each case just be an explosion pit due to the bubble of hot gases generated. For this reason the craters all tend to be more or less circular and have no tendency to reflect in their shape the variations in the incident directions that must have occurred.

What had prompted many investigators in the past to try to find an interpretation other than in terms of impacts was the fact that such a

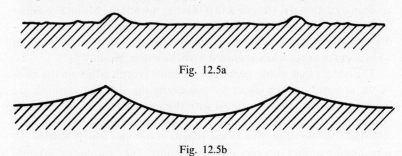

Fig. 12.5a

Fig. 12.5b

terrific bombardment was not considered a likely part of the history of the Moon. With the type of theory of the origin of the solar system that we have discussed, in which multiple collisions play a major part, we would indeed expect each of the bodies to be covered with impact craters. In the case of the Earth, we have found a reason why they can no longer be seen very clearly. On the Moon nothing has occurred to obliterate them.

Let us now discuss what more can be understood about the surface from the investigation of the impact craters. On the higher ground craters overlap craters (Fig. 12.3), and this furnishes a way of deciding on relative dates. If there are two craters that overlap each other, then the one with the unbroken rim is the younger and the one whose rim has been broken into is the older. In fact, overlaps of great multiciplicity can be seen and in some places it is possible to arrange five or six craters in a time sequence. In the very many examples of this sort it is invariably found that the older craters have, for a given size, a much lower height of rim and a much more rounded profile of the crater edge (see Fig. 12.5a and 12.5b). Also, it is these that very frequently have the remarkably flat interior floor. This evident correlation between the age and the sharpness of the features could either be due to a progressive change in the process of formation of the craters or to some sort of erosion. The first possibility does not seem compatible with the impact explosion theory, as these extremely shallow craters, possessing no more than a gentle hill surrounding a huge flat plain, could not have resulted directly from an explosion. An erosion process that has degraded the old craters clearly requires to be investigated further.

The quantities of material that would have to have been moved by such an erosion process are by no means small. A large proportion of the surface area of the high ground is occupied by crater walls which must at one time have been 2 or 3 km higher than they now are. A large amount of material is missing and if this has not left the Moon altogether it has to be identified with some parts of the present surface. The quantity of material that must have been moved might well be of the order of 1 km average depth when averaged over the whole Moon.

The craters that would be judged the most recent, either on the basis of the criterion of overlap or by possessing the sharpest features, are frequently found to be associated with the so-called 'rays'. The rays are best seen at full moon (see Fig. 12.1). These are features that must have originated at the same time as the parent crater and which overlay the surrounding surface to a very small depth only. They are almost certainly the deposit of small particles scattered by the explosion, as occurs around bomb craters. The fact that these disappear comparatively quickly also requires some erosion process to be operative on every type of ground.

The obvious suggestion would be that the flat bottoms of many of the older craters, and generally the flat type of ground that is seen in the maria, represents the eroded material which has been so deposited by some sedimentation process. This runs counter to the point of view that has been adopted by most other investigators of the lunar surface. At the time when the craters were thought to be of volcanic origin, the flat regions were thought of as solidified lava flows. Volcanism was then given up as a theory of the crater formation, but the idea of the lava flows has mostly remained. There seem to be, however, many arguments against the lava hypothesis. By comparison with lava flows on the Earth, these would be very much bigger and much flatter. Much greater volumes of lava would have had to be poured out at one time, and with much greater fluidity, than ever occurred on the Earth, and yet the remaining solid surface, as we have said, suffered incomparably smaller deformations only. On the Earth, small amounts of volcanism are associated with mountain-building processes during which great distortions by hundreds of miles have taken place in large regions. On the Moon it would be necessary to suppose that there was enough lava present close below the surface to puncture and penetrate into many craters long after they were formed and flow to a flat surface inside, and at the same time not cause any distortion of the part of the surface remaining solid.

The supposed lava flows would seem to have occurred in most cases much later than the formation of the craters which they flooded, as we can see by the number of subsequent small impacts that have occurred on the rim and in the interior. We find that, in general, the number is much greater on the rim. Each individual impact can thus not have been directly responsible for the flooding, but it would be necessary to think that each crater bowl later became a weak spot through which lava could get to the surface. This would have to apply to very many craters of very different sizes, and yet the enormous hydrostatic unbalance that is necessary for this process could only have shown itself in any other way. Quite unreasonable material strengths are involved to allow this to occur. All the flooding must have occurred at a temperature well above the melting-point of lava if the generation of steep lava slopes so common on Earth is to be completely avoided. The lava generation process, which has by now evidently stopped completely, must not have gone through a phase in which it was weaker so that it could only force up some amounts of viscous material in a few places, for such an activity would have produced recognizable features which are not, in fact, found. If there are some volcanic cones on the Moon, it is certainly only a very small number and there are certainly none as large as many on the Earth. There is certainly not a single active volcano of the normal terrestrial sort on the Moon now, although there may well be places where gas is escaping from the Moon's interior through some cracks.

The alternative explanation which one can pursue is, therefore, that an erosion process occurs which breaks up the surface material into very fine powder and stirs up this powder on the surface in such a way that a thin surface layer is, in fact, capable of flowing downhill. Any repeated agitation of the surface dust would, of course, have this consequence. One has, of course, to bear in mind that the time scales for the Moon are a great deal longer than for erosion processes on the Earth and one is, therefore, forced to investigate extremely slight effects. Of all the forces that might be applied in lunar conditions to a dust grain, electrostatic forces would seem to be by far the largest.

Any erratic charging such as would occur by bombardment with energetic charge particles would tend to make dust grains jump when the mutual repulsion exceeded the weight of a grain. It is, in fact, possible to demonstrate in the laboratory that a fine rock powder when bombarded by electrons of kilovolt energies or higher does behave in this way. We know now that great quantities of energetic particles from the Sun are bombarding the Moon, and quantitatively the effect may well be enough to have shifted kilometres of dust in three or four thousand million years. Many detailed points can be discussed in terms of such a dust flow hypothesis and there seems to be no conflict with the observational data. One can therefore regard the Moon as a body in whose interior the heat generation was inadequate to cause widespread melting and the consequent gravitational sorting out of materials. Perhaps the remarkably low mean density of the Moon is due to the inability of the volatile constituents like water to percolate through the solid material without the cracks and the veins which we suppose to have existed in the case of the Earth. The large departure from hydrostatic equilibrium which the shape of the Moon displays is also in better accord with a solid Moon than with one in which huge amounts of lava have existed at one time.

Observation of thermal radiation from the Moon's surface has made clear that a substantial proportion is covered with a material of extremely low heat content and very low heat conductivity. This again points to dust. Radar observations have shown that the Moon's surface is remarkably smooth down to a scale of irregularity of about 10 cm. The gradients that occur on this small scale are not very much steeper than those that can be seen with an optical resolution of a kilometre. Again, an erosion process must be thought of to smooth out the many small steep features that the impacts would have left behind. When we see the Moon from close up it will be mostly very gentle smooth slopes that we shall see and none, or extremely little, of the jagged steep mountains that have been the usual artist's conception of the lunar surface.

CHAPTER 13

Conclusion

The lunar surface and the meteorite evidence is certainly the best material we have for finding out more about the detailed processes of the past. Let us look at the meteorite evidence in a little more detail now. The most common type of meteorite, as we have said, is one composed mainly of the heavier silicates pervaded with nickel–iron veins. It is quite clear that it must have come from a major body and it must have been sufficiently hot at one time for the metal and some silicates to be liquid while the bulk of the material was solid. This is just the condition in which we had to have the mantle of the Earth in order that it should appear seismically solid and at the same time allow the gradual formation of an iron core and a light crust. A similar condition must have existed on the body or bodies from which this material was exploded off by violent impacts some three to five thousand million years ago.

It could, of course, be that some of this was material that was removed from the primitive Earth or Mars or perhaps more likely from another body which, like many others, did not survive the period of the big collisions. Some of these bodies must indeed have had iron–nickel cores like the Earth and were then smashed up so completely that pieces of clean iron–nickel alloy exist on orbits in the solar system and occasionally come in as meteorites. If in these earlier generations of bodies the sorting-out processes had taken place, then it is clear that the greatest quantity of meteoritic material should have been formed from the mantle, for it comprises nine-tenths or so of the volume; a very small fraction from the thin crust, and perhaps one-tenth from the iron of the core. Not all meteorites need then be of the same age, for the great collisions must have occurred over quite an extended period. Meteorites that have only spent a comparatively short time since being broken off in the collision of asteroids might occur; but it would be very unlikely for meteorites to show a small age since the time that they were deep in the interior of a larger body, for we think that the period of the heavy bombardment was over before the commencement of most of the geological record on the Earth. The meteoritic evidence is very much in favour of the kind of theory we discussed in earlier chapters for the origin of the solar system and for the interior of the Earth. Indeed, it hardly seems possible that it could be accounted for in any other way.

What more will we learn when we investigate other planets? We have now seen the back of the Moon, and no doubt this was a warming-up exercise for obtaining pictures one day of the surface of Mars from nearby. Mars is much smaller than the Earth, but larger than the Moon. One might expect, therefore, that it has suffered less of the mountain-building processes than the Earth, and that therefore more of the lunar-type surface will be showing, with the large circular markings still visible. Since there is an atmosphere on Mars, there will have been erosion on a much greater scale than on the Moon, and we cannot estimate to what extent this will have obliterated the original features; but if those can still be seen it will allow one to establish more firmly a theory of the Earth's surface. Clearly nothing could be better for this than to see a planet in which the same processes had taken place as on the Earth, but to a different extent.

Venus, whose surface we have not yet seen because of the permanent cloud cover, is similar in mass to the Earth, and although the surface chemistry, the atmosphere, and therefore the erosion, are very different, one might expect that the processes of continental growth have proceeded there as far as on Earth. It is an exciting possibility that this might yet be discovered by earthbound radar before any vehicles can be lowered through the clouds of the planet.

The possibility of the existence of very large numbers of planetary systems around other stars introduces particular interest in the question of the origin of life. We may find some form of life on Mars, and many investigators think this very probable. If, by its biochemical analysis, this proves to be of different origin from the terrestrial life, there will be a demonstration of a high probability existing for the generation of life on suitable planets, and the probability would then be high for the presence of life on vast numbers of other planetary systems.

These are the problems which, together with many others, will be tackled by modern research. They seem to me as exciting as any that have ever been considered in any field of human endeavour.

CHAPTER 14

The Origin of Cosmic Radiation

Cosmic radiation was discovered by Hess just before the beginning of the First World War. His discovery was the consequence of a number of previous observations, the first and most elementary of which was the observation that a Gold Leaf Electroscope will not hold its charge indefinitely. Even when the insulation is made as good as possible the charge will eventually leak away and the gold leaves fall together. It was found, eventually, that this discovery was due in the first place to the fact that gases themselves are not perfect insulators, but that they can be ionized and to some extent then conduct electricity.

When radioactivity was discovered it was found that the rays from radioactive substances can be very effective in ionizing gases and since, over land, most of the surroundings contain a certain amount of radioactive substances, some explanation of this effect was obtained. However, observations over sea showed that the amount of ionization produced is about half as great as over land, although sea water contains very little radioactivity.

As a consequence of this observation a series of measurements on high towers was made and it was found that although ionization decreases with height above ground to begin with, it does not decrease as fast as one would expect if all the ionization were due to radioactivity from the ground. Continuing this sort of observation Hess took ionization chambers in balloons to great heights and found that, far from decreasing, the amount of ionization increased very considerably when one got to heights above 10,000 ft. He drew the conclusion, which has since been found to be correct, that this ionization was caused by a penetrating radiation coming from outer space. The consequences of this discovery, which started out in such a simple way, have been very considerable. Further investigation of cosmic radiation showed that the energies of the particles coming in from outer space were very great and that they could produce nuclear disintegrations in the atmosphere and also in materials at sea-level. One rather remarkable consequence of these nuclear disintegrations is that some of the nitrogen in the atmosphere is converted to radioactive carbon. This radioactive carbon has a half life of about 5000 years, and it is ingested along with normal carbon by plants and, of course, in turn by any animal which eats these plants, so that part of the carbon in all living things is radioactive carbon. Now when a tree dies it ceases to take in the radioactive carbon and, because of decay, the proportion of radioactive to normal carbon, falls. By measuring this proportion one can determine the length of time which has elapsed since the tree died. This discovery has had very considerable consequences in archaeology and in the geology of recent periods. It is now possible, for instance, to date with considerable accuracy wooden objects from the pyramids of Ancient Egypt or clothing from Danish peat bogs or bones from Pueblo Indian tombs.

Yet another consequence of the high-energy nuclear interactions produced by cosmic radiation is that part of the energy is transformed into previously unknown and often unstable particles. The first new particle which was discovered was the positron, a counterpart of the ordinary negative electron but with positive charge. Shortly after this discovery in 1936, Anderson, working in California, discovered a heavy particle, the μ-meson, which had a lifetime of about a millionth of a second. Just after World War II the π-meson with a lifetime of the order of only one hundred-millionth of a second was discovered by Professor Powell in Bristol, and soon the strange K-mesons and hyperons (particles whose mass is greater than that of protons) were also found.

In quite another direction cosmic radiation has been studied in connection with geomagnetic effects and solar physics. It was found early on that the chief component of cosmic radiation was positively charged and that particles were deflected in the magnetic field of the Earth as they approached the Earth. These sort of effects have been studied in considerable detail and very recently, using satellites, the great radiation belts, called after Professor Van Allen who first found them, have been discovered. From an even wider point of view one finds that astrophysicists are interested in cosmic radiation because as we shall see, a great part of this radiation must originate outside the solar system. Now let us try and see what is known at the present moment about the cosmic radiation.

In the first place, the energies of the cosmic ray particles extend over a very wide range. The energy attained by a singly charged particle in falling through a potential of one thousand million volts is 1 BeV. The energies of cosmic ray protons vary from a few tenths of 1 BeV up to at least 100,000,000 BeV. More energetic particles occur more rarely and the fall-off in numbers as the energy increases is steep. For every million particles of energy 10 BeV there is only one of energy about 20,000 BeV.

As a consequence of this we know a great deal more about low-energy cosmic radiation than about high-energy cosmic radiation. At the very highest energies one may have to wait for months before one can detect a single event.

Now let us consider the nature of the particles. Here, at comparatively low energies, of, say, about 10 BeV per nucleon, a good deal is known. Most of the cosmic ray particles are protons, the second most important components are the nuclei of helium often called 'alpha particles', and then there are other nuclei which are at least as heavy as iron. The actual proportions are shown in Table 14.1.

Table 14.1. The approximate composition of the cosmic radiation at energies of about 10 BeV per nucleon

Element	H	He	Li, Be and B	C, N, O and Ne	Mg, Si, S and A	Fe
	90·1	9·01	0·16 (?)	0·60	0·09	0·04

One very interesting feature is that there seemed to be very few electrons in the primary beam. It is possible that there are some high-energy gamma rays, but as yet this has not been proved. At the higher energies we know something about the composition, but the proportions are not at all accurately known. Up to energies of about 1,000,000 BeV, cosmic ray particles can be detected occasionally in photographic emulsions flown high in the atmosphere from balloons, and up to these energies we know that protons and alpha particles are still present, and we suspect also that heavy nuclei occur. The most energetic disintegration yet seen in a photographic emulsion was produced by an alpha particle. One difficulty in the use of this method for studying the composition at high energies is that the balloons can only be flown to a certain height in the atmosphere and that, even at the highest, there is still an appreciable amount of atmosphere above them. Now, the heavier the nucleus the greater its cross-section, and hence the more likely it is to make a collision with a nucleus in the air, so that if we had very heavy nuclei coming in they might easily be removed from the beam before reaching balloon altitudes. This would be particularly so if the cross-section for disintegration increased with increasing primary energy. Hence even at these energies, around 100,000 to 1,000,000 BeV, we are not at all certain of the composition. Above this energy we can only really guess about what constitutes the primary cosmic radiation. The most conservative hypothesis is that the composition is not very different from what it is for low energies, that is to say, we have protons, alpha particles, and heavier nuclei present. There are a number of lines of evidence which suggest that the proportion of heavy primaries may be greater at these high energies. For example, in the cores of air showers, a number of high-energy nucleons have sometimes been seen and these might well result from the break-up of the heavy primary particle near the top of the atmosphere.

Another very interesting series of observations has been made on the rates at which different sorts of cosmic ray particles occur. Again we know a good deal about the sort of thing that can happen when the primaries are of comparatively low energy. For a long time it was thought that even in this region the rates were constant, but now it is known that changes take place quite often and that some of these changes are very spectacular. For example, it has been found that sometimes when large flares occur on the Sun, very big changes in cosmic ray rates occur afterwards on Earth. The types of cosmic ray which are detected in order to see this sort of effect are the μ-mesons and the neutrons which reach sea-level. There are two types of apparatus used, one consists of a number of trays of Geiger counters separated by lead, these detect the passage of μ-mesons through the arrangement. The other, called the neutron monitor, has a number of Geiger counters filled with an isotope of boron, to make them respond to neutrons, and embedded in lead and paraffin. On occasions, these neutron monitors have been found to increase their counting rates up to about 3000 per

Table 14·2

Timetable of events associated with the large solar flare of February 23rd, 1956

Time	Event
03.31	Onset of strong optical flare.
03.32	Onset of solar radio outburst at 3000 Mc/sec.
03.35	Onset of solar radio outburst at 200 Mc/sec.
	Onset of sudden ionospheric disturbance.
03.42	Maximum optical intensity of the flare.
	Onset of cosmic ray increase in the combined impact zone.
03.47	Onset of cosmic ray increase in the third impact zone.
03.49	Maximum of cosmic ray intensity in the combined impact zone.
03.53	Onset of cosmic ray increase in the polar regions.
03.55 to 04.10	Maximum of cosmic ray intensity in the third impact zone.
04.15	End of the optical flare.
04.15 to 04.18	Maximum of cosmic ray intensity in the polar regions.
04.30	Isotropic distribution and gradual decrease of cosmic ray intensity.

cent of the normal rate in a very short time. These increases are always correlated with the occurrence of big flares on the Sun. Table 14.2 shows a typical time sequence for one of these flares, the flare of February 23rd, 1956. First one sees the visible flare on the Sun followed almost at the same time by an outburst of radio noise and then eight or nine minutes later a sudden increase of the cosmic ray intensities in certain zones of the Earth. After the enormous sudden increase, the cosmic ray intensity falls for six or seven hours until it is more or less back to normal. Five of these big flares have been seen so far and the last one in 1956 was observed at many stations throughout the world, so that a good deal is now known about this phenomenon.

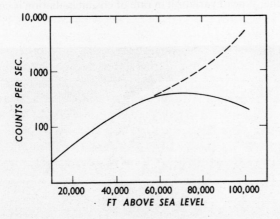

Fig. 14.1. This shows the normal change in counting rate as a Geiger counter rises through the atmosphere, and, in the dotted curve, the abnormal change following the solar flare of July, 1959

Recently, it has been found that there are big cosmic ray increases near the top of the atmosphere associated with smaller solar flares. In two balloon flights at Minnesota it was found that within a period of seven hours the rate of cosmic ray protons increased by a factor of 200. Even more recently Dr. Robert Brown, at Berkeley, California, has found three large cosmic ray increases, all associated with solar flares within one week. One of these increases is shown in Fig. 14.1, and a large solar flare in Fig. 14.2. The first curve on the figure shows the normal change in the cosmic ray counting rate as one flies the Geiger counter telescope from sea-level to about 100,000 ft. First there is the very big increase in counting rate which was noticed by Hess and which caused the discovery of cosmic radiation, then the radiation reaches a maximum and above that it begins to fall again as the top of the atmosphere is approached. This maximum is called the Pfotzer maximum after its discoverer. On the occasions after the flares no such maximum was seen and the cosmic ray intensity continued to increase as far as the balloon could go. It is very interesting to note that if one extrapolates this curve to the top of the atmosphere one finds that the radiation dosage there would be about 600 roentgens per hour. Now 600 is a fatal dose, so that any astronaut caught in such a burst of cosmic radiation would have to seek some form of shelter quickly. This sort of effect and, of course, the great radiation belts, have led Dr. Brown to remark that 'space is not safe'.

Yet another type of variation in rate of cosmic radiation is correlated

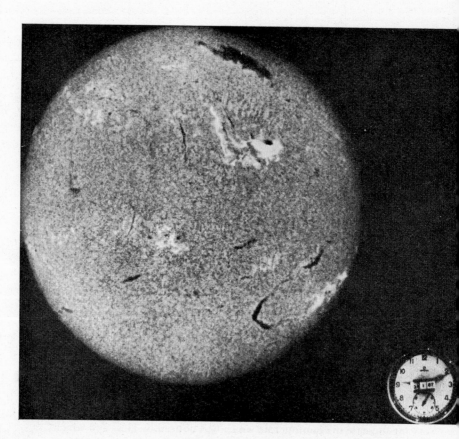

Fig. 14.2. A large solar flare. The photograph is due to Dr. Giovanelli of C.S.I.R.O.

with the solar cycle, that is to say, as the number of sun spots varies from maximum to minimum one finds that there is a change in the intensity of cosmic radiation received by some parts of the Earth. There are, in fact, a number of other possible variations in rates which appear to be correlated with the activity of the Sun.

At higher energies the picture is not so clear. In fact, many people think that the rates of all types of high-energy cosmic radiation are constant with time, and the intensities coming from different parts of space are equal. Many of the experiments which have been performed are consistent with this viewpoint, but, on the other hand, because of the very low counting rates with which one has to deal when one is working with high energies, these results are also consistent with a number of other possibilities.

These high-energy particles are detected by what are called 'extensive air showers'. When a very high-energy cosmic ray primary hits the top of the atmosphere it produces a nuclear collision from which there may emerge a considerable number of secondary particles. These secondary particles themselves have very high energies and, in turn, may make collisions. In this way a sort of cascade process develops so that when the shower reaches sea-level there may be a million or ten million particles in it. Such a shower of particles can be detected by suitable arrangements of Geiger counters or scintillation counters. A picture of a small portion of such a shower is shown in Fig. 14.3. However, if one sets up a normal array of Geiger counters then it will respond to extensive air showers coming from almost any direction. In fact, because of the atmosphere, one rarely sees extensive air showers coming from directions greater than 30° from the vertical, but even so the array accepts all showers within this angle so that it is not particularly sensitive to direction. If one looks at the heavens with this sort of device, it is equivalent to using a type of optical telescope which integrates the light received over a 30° cone. Obviously visual astronomy would not have found out much about star distributions if it had been limited to the use of such telescopes. By various devices, for example, by using Wilson cloud chambers to photograph the directions of the particles in the shower, the array can be made much more directional. Fig. 14.3 shows a picture of an extensive air shower taken with a Wilson cloud chamber and it can be seen that the direction of the shower through the cloud chamber can be determined with some accuracy. In fact, with this sort of arrangement one can often find the direction of the shower to about ±3°. Even so this means that the shower could have come from quite a considerable area of sky, say 6° × 6°. When one remembers that

U.O.–I*

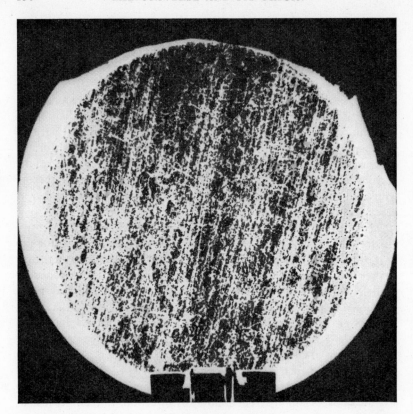

Fig. 14.3. A Wilson cloud chamber photograph of a small portion of an extensive
air shower

the angles subtended by the full Moon are about a quarter of a square
degree, one realizes that even this device does not measure angles with
any great precision. Hence at very high energies, with a low counting
rate and the bad angular resolution, we cannot yet say much about the
variation in intensity of the radiation, either over the sky or with time.

Having considered these known facts about cosmic radiation, let us
look at some of the theories of its origin. First of all, it seems obvious
from what we have seen that there must be more than one source of
cosmic radiation. In the first place, because of the correlation of many of
the phenomena at low energies with events on the Sun, the Sun itself
must be able to accelerate cosmic rays to these energies. However, it is
not easy to see how the Sun can accelerate particles to the very high
energies. It seems likely that protons of energy of at least 10,000,000 BeV

occur in the primary cosmic radiation. If such a proton is moving in a magnetic field of 10^{-5} Gauss its radius of curvature is three light years, so that such a proton could hardly be contained in the solar system. Moreover, it is fairly easy to calculate the amount of energy which the Sun puts into cosmic radiation. If one does this, one finds that the energy stored even in low-energy cosmic radiation is very much greater than can be accounted for by the output of all the stars in the galaxy, assuming that they have the same activity as the Sun. So although the Sun does accelerate some low-energy cosmic radiation, it cannot account for all the low-energy cosmic radiation or for any of the really high-energy cosmic radiation.

To get over this difficulty, Fermi supposed that most of the acceleration of cosmic radiation occurred in the space between the stars. His basic idea was quite simple. It is known that between the stars in the plane of the galaxy there are large clouds of dust and gas, and that associated with these there are magnetic fields. Fermi supposed that when the high-energy cosmic ray particle was moving through space it would collide with these magnetic fields and be deflected. If the fields were moving towards the cosmic ray particle, this would result in an increase of its energy due to the collision; if the fields were moving away, then the particle would lose energy. This is exactly the same situation as if one threw a tennis ball at a steam roller: if the steam roller was moving towards you the tennis ball would gain energy; if away, it would lose it. Since, when the field and the particle are moving together their relative velocity is greater, one finds, on average, that 'head-on' collisions occur more frequently than overtaking collisions, and hence on average, cosmic ray particles gain rather than lose energy. However, although this idea is basically quite sound, it has been found that in order to accelerate the cosmic ray particle in a sufficiently short time, the velocities of the clouds and the magnetic fields would have to be a good deal higher than, in fact, they are on average, in the plane of the galaxy. Hence people have looked for other situations where this basic idea of Fermi's might be expected to work.

One of the most likely of these situations is in the envelope of expanding gas around the Supernova. Fig. 14.4 shows the shell of expanding gas from the Supernova of 1054 A.D. Supernova are stars which suddenly build up and turn from small dim objects to objects whose light emission is temporarily as great as a whole galaxy. They are in themselves extremely interesting objects and they are particularly interesting when one considers the circumstances in which one believes the explosion to take place. They are also interesting because the light which they emit

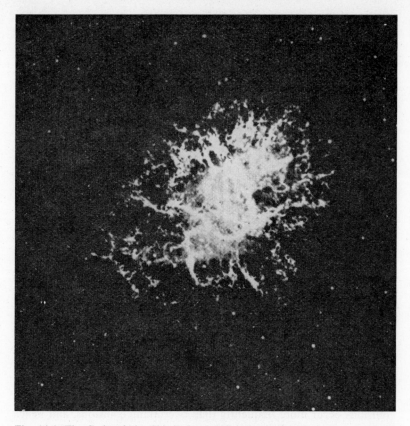

Fig. 14.4. The Crab nebula. This is the turbulent expanding shell of gas from the
explosion of the Supernova of 1054 A.D.

can best be explained as synchrotron radiation. The radiation which
they give off would be typical of that produced by electrons of energy
from 100 to 1000 BeV moving in magnetic fields of 10^{-3} Gauss. This
theory, which now has a good deal of experimental evidence to support
it, was put forward by two Russian astrophysicists, Ginsburg and
Schlovski. So we know now that in the envelopes of the Supernova we
have certainly these high-energy electrons and, if such high-energy
electrons existed, then it is extremely likely that protons of an even
higher energy will occur, say from 100,000 to 1,000,000 BeV, and that
heavy nuclei, at least as heavy as iron, of energies between 5,600,000 to
56,000,000 BeV will occur. A very interesting theory of this type of
Supernova has been put forward by Burbridge and his co-workers. It has

been observed that the light from a new Supernova of this type decays within a period of fifty-five days, and Burbridge has explained this by supposing that the light is due to the isotope of Californium, of mass 254. They believe that the Supernova starts out as a star which is deficient in hydrogen. It is because of this deficiency that the tremendous explosion eventually takes place. During this explosion the heavy elements which originally made up a much bigger proportion of the star than is usual, built up into Californium 254. It is known that build-up into this particular heavy element can happen in these very rapid processes because Californium itself was first discovered in the debris left behind by the first hydrogen bomb. Californium decays by spontaneous fission and the two products of this fission will both be moderately heavy elements such as rhenium or iodine (or neighbouring elements in the periodic table). Two fragments from the fission will have a fairly high initial energy, and in the shell of very turbulent gas produced by the explosion there will be very big magnetic fields of the order 100-1000 Gauss. Thus one has all the conditions for the rapid application of the Fermi acceleration mechanism. One of these Supernova occur about every 300 years in each galaxy and, because of the long storage time of cosmic radiation in the galaxy, this might well be sufficient to account for the observed cosmic radiation intensity. A number of other peculiar stars may also contribute to the flux of cosmic radiation. Of these, the most likely are the Blue Super Giants, Wolf-Rayet stars, and magnetic variable stars. From these sources one may well be able to account for all cosmic radiation of total energy up to about 1,000,000,000 BeV. However, if, as is possible, cosmic ray particles of even higher energy occur, then one must look for other sources. It seems very difficult to confine such very high cosmic rays to our galaxy, even if one allows them to be stored in the halo of Population II stars around the galaxy, and this has led some authors to suggest that the ultra high-energy cosmic rays are from outside our galaxy.

There is a very peculiar object in the galaxy called Messier 87. This is about 2000 light years long and, like the Crab nebulae, its light is thought to be due to the synchrotron radiation of high-energy electrons in magnetic fields. Because of its enormous dimensions acceleration of cosmic radiation to very high energies indeed might occur in this jet. Yet another possibility is that the really high-energy cosmic rays are accelerated in colliding galaxies. When two galaxies collide, the stars in general pass through without any encounters. But the gas between the stars in the two galaxies has a very high viscosity (remembering the very large scale on which these events happen), so it becomes very turbulent, large magnetic fields are produced, acceleration takes place and a great deal of radio emission occurs. Under these circumstances it seems very likely that cosmic ray particles also could be accelerated to high energies.

Thus, in general, we may suppose that there are a large number of sources of cosmic radiation. Since the Sun produces some cosmic radiation, it is almost certain that all stars like the Sun also do so, and that more active stars will produce more radiation than does the Sun. We have seen that Supernova can produce very considerable amounts of radiation (and of high energy), and finally that the highest energies may be produced by peculiar objects like the jet of M87 or colliding galaxies. Thus, cosmic radiation most likely does not come from one particular source but from a variety of sources and the acceleration of charged particles to high energies may be a very usual phenomenon in space.

When cosmic radiation has been accelerated it generally travels a considerable distance and for a considerable time before it reaches the Earth. As we have seen, it is very likely that in interstellar space there are a number of magnetic fields. Unless a cosmic ray particle is of extremely high energy it will be appreciably deflected by these fields. For example, if it is a proton of energy 100,000 BeV it will have a radius of curvature of one-thirtieth of a light year in a field of 10^{-5} Gauss. Thus, such particles can be expected to travel in very complicated curved paths and to be 'scrambled' in their passage through interstellar space from the source origin of the Earth. In fact, if we study the intensities of 100,000 BeV protons coming from various directions of the sky and if we find their intensities to be different, then this would reflect the local magnetic fields immediately around the solar system rather than the distribution of sources of cosmic radiation in the sky. As the energy we study increases, this becomes less and less so and finally if 10,000,000,000 BeV protons exist, we could expect these to move through our galaxy without very much deflection, and a study of the intensities of such particles might well enable us to decide from which of the extra-galactic objects they come.

INDEX